COMPUTATIONAL MODELING AND SIMULATIONS OF BIOMOLECULAR SYSTEMS

COMPUTATIONAL MODELING AND SIMULATIONS OF BIOMOLECULAR SYSTEMS

Benoît Roux

The University of Chicago, USA

World Scientific

NEW JERSEY · LONDON · SINGAPORE · BEIJING · SHANGHAI · HONG KONG · TAIPEI · CHENNAI · TOKYO

Published by

World Scientific Publishing Co. Pte. Ltd.

5 Toh Tuck Link, Singapore 596224

USA office: 27 Warren Street, Suite 401-402, Hackensack, NJ 07601

UK office: 57 Shelton Street, Covent Garden, London WC2H 9HE

British Library Cataloguing-in-Publication Data
A catalogue record for this book is available from the British Library.

ISBN 978-981-123-275-6 (hardcover)
ISBN 978-981-123-276-3 (ebook for institutions)
ISBN 978-981-123-277-0 (ebook for individuals)

For any available supplementary material, please visit
https://www.worldscientific.com/worldscibooks/10.1142/12173#t=suppl

Typeset by Stallion Press
Email: enquiries@stallionpress.com

To Muriel, Miah, and Alazne.

Preface

This textbook originated from the course "Simulation, Modeling, and Computations in Biophysics" that I have taught at the University of Chicago since 2011. The students typically came from a wide range of backgrounds, including biology, physics, chemistry, biochemistry, and mathematics, and the course was intentionally adapted for senior undergraduate students and graduate students. Over the years, the students provided invaluable feedback that tremendously helped organize and pace the material covered in the course. From the start, the goal was not to teach a highly technical course dedicated to specialists, but to travel in one broad sweep from the physical description of a complex molecular system at the most fundamental level, to the type of phenomenological models commonly used to represent the function of large biological macromolecular machines. The key conceptual elements serving as building blocks in the formulation of different levels of approximations are introduced along the way, aiming to clarify as much as possible how they are interrelated. The only assumption is a basic familiarity with simple mathematics (calculus and integrals, ordinary differential equations, matrix linear algebra, and Fourier–Laplace transforms).

The interesting journey of understanding biological macromolecular systems on the basis of physics begins by considering the evolution one such system in the language of quantum mechanics with the Schrödinger equation (Chapter 1). This picture is exploited to introduce many of the approximations used in classical molecular dynamics simulations based on empirical force fields. This is followed by an introduction of basic concepts of energy conservation, statistical mechanics, and the Maxwell–Boltzmann distribution (Chapters 2–4), with a particular focus on the reversible work theorem, the potential of mean force, the solvation free energy, and implicit solvent models leading to a discussion of Poisson–Boltzmann theory. This first part of the book dedicated to equilibrium properties concludes with the treatment of noncovalent association and standard binding free energy in Chapter 5. The book then switches gears in Chapter 6 to introduce kinetic and dynamical properties, time-correlation functions, and Green–Kubo linear response (some of this material is a little more advanced and could be covered at a later stage). These concepts are leveraged in Chapters 7 and 8 to introduce the concept of effective nondeterministic dynamics to represent the evolution of a reduced set of degrees of freedom that is part of a large complex system. Because of the unaccounted missing degrees of freedom, effective dynamics of reduced models typically displays an unpredictable random and stochastic character such as with Brownian dynamics and Langevin dynamics. These provide important frameworks for representing a wide range of dynamical processes in complex molecular systems. Chapter 9 deals with the classic concept of rare transitions between two stable states occurring on a very long timescale. This idea is immediately expanded and generalized in Chapter 10 by introducing kinetic models with multiple discrete states to represent the dynamical evolution of a complex system. This class of models are called discrete-state continuous-time Markov chains, in which the probability of the transition from one state to another does not depend on the previous history of the system. Having elaborated on a wide class of effective dynamical of reduced models, Chapter 11 deals with many of the practicalities to simulate those with computers using so-called pseudo-random number generators. Illustrations include the treatment of Metropolis Monte Carlo, reactive flux dynamics, Brownian dynamics, Langevin dynamics, and Markov chains. The book ends in Chapter 12, to review the main ingredients involved in the construction of phenomenological multistate models used to represent the function of large biological macromolecular machines. Illustrative examples using the paradigm of membrane transport systems are discussed. It is my sincere hope that the textbook will serve as a springboard to inspire young scientists to advance physics-based modeling in novel and creative ways.

Benoît Roux

Acknowledgments

I am very much indebted to my students who patiently sat through my lectures and provided tremendous feedback on the material. A special thanks to Allen Zhu for his personal notes in Latex format. I am especially grateful to Giovanni Ciccotti, John Straub, Chris Chipot, Fabian Paul, and Suriyanarayanan Vaikuntanathan who provided sound advice in numerous instances. Much appreciated proof reading was done by Lydia Blachowicz, Manish Gupta, and Max Rempell. Jing Li, Moeen Meigooni, and Emad Tajkhorshid helped with the molecular graphics pictures.

Contents

Chapter 1

Representation of molecular systems

Let us envision a large biological macromolecular system. For example, the system may comprise a protein embedded in a phospholipid bilayer membrane, surrounded by a large number of water molecules and ions. A typical system is schematically illustrated in Figure 1.1. We seek to describe the evolution and behavior of such biological macromolecular systems at the most fundamental level based on the laws of physics. The most realistic and detailed description would involve the quantum mechanical (QM) nature of the microscopic world. This means that the evolution of the atom nuclei and electrons of the biological macromolecular system must be represented through the time-dependent nuclear–electronic wave function $\Psi(\mathbf{R}_1, \ldots, \mathbf{R}_N, \mathbf{r}_1, \ldots, \mathbf{r}_n, t)$, which is obtained by solving the time-dependent Schrödinger equation [Merzbacher (1998)],

$$i\hbar \frac{\partial}{\partial t} \Psi(\mathbf{R}_1, \ldots, \mathbf{R}_N, \mathbf{r}_1, \ldots, \mathbf{r}_n, t) = \hat{\mathcal{H}} \Psi(\mathbf{R}_1, \ldots, \mathbf{R}_N, \mathbf{r}_1, \ldots, \mathbf{r}_n, t) \quad (1.1)$$

where the Hamiltonian $\hat{\mathcal{H}}$ is

$$\hat{\mathcal{H}} = \sum_i \frac{\mathbf{P}_i^2}{2M_i} + \sum_i \frac{\mathbf{p}_i^2}{2m_i} - \sum_{i,j} \frac{z_i e^2}{\|\mathbf{R}_i - \mathbf{r}_j\|} + \sum_{i<j} \frac{z_i z_j}{\|\mathbf{R}_i - \mathbf{R}_j\|} + \sum_{i<j} \frac{e^2}{\|\mathbf{r}_i - \mathbf{r}_j\|}$$

$$(1.2)$$

(For the sake of clarity, we will use uppercase $\mathbf{R}_i$ and $\mathbf{P}_i$ for the nuclei, and lowercase $\mathbf{r}_i$ and $\mathbf{p}_i$ for the electrons in this argument.) The Schrödinger equation is a differential equation for the wave function. The first term in the Hamiltonian is the kinetic energy of the nuclei, which is defined in terms of the momentum operator of the i-th nuclei, $\mathbf{P}_i = \frac{\hbar}{i} \nabla_i$, and the second term is the kinetic energy of the electron, which is defined in

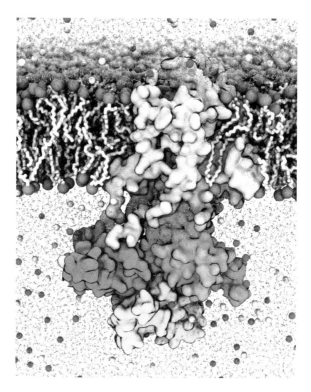

Fig. 1.1   Schematic representation of an instantaneous configuration (snapshot) of a large biological macromolecular system comprising a protein, a phospholipid membrane, water molecules and ions. The protein here is the sarco/endoplasmic reticulum Ca^{2+}-ATPase (SERCA), an ion pump that actively transports Ca^{2+} ions across the sarcoplasmic reticulum membrane in muscle cells to create an ion concentration gradient. The ions are K^+ (magenta) and Cl^- (yellow). The figure was prepared using the program VMD [Humphrey *et al.* (1996)].

terms of the momentum operator of the i-th electron, $\mathbf{p}_i = \frac{\hbar}{i}\nabla_i$. The last terms in $\hat{\mathcal{H}}$ represent the Coulomb interactions between the charged nuclei and electrons. Constructing a time-dependent wave function for all particles (nuclei and electrons) in a large system in a thorough and rigorous manner is prohibitively complex. To paraphrase Dirac (1929), even though the underlying quantum mechanical laws are known, the difficulty is that these laws lead to equations that are *"much too complicated to be soluble"* in the case of complex molecular systems. This makes it necessary to develop *"approximate practical methods of applying quantum mechanics"* that can be applied to explain the main features of such systems without too much computation.

1.1 The Born–Oppenheimer approximation

The Born–Oppenheimer (BO) approximation exploits the fact that the mass of the electron is much smaller than the mass of any of the nuclei [Merzbacher (1998)]. For a proton, which is the lightest nucleus, the ratio, $m_p/m_e \approx 1836$. Based on the BO approximation, we introduce the electronic Hamiltonian, $\hat{\mathcal{H}}_e$, which depends parametrically on the position of the *fixed* nuclei,

$$\hat{\mathcal{H}}_e = \sum_i \frac{\mathbf{p}_i^2}{2m_i} - \sum_{i,j} \frac{z_i e^2}{\|\mathbf{R}_i - \mathbf{r}_j\|} + \sum_{i<j} \frac{z_i z_j}{\|\mathbf{R}_i - \mathbf{R}_j\|} + \sum_{i<j} \frac{e^2}{\|\mathbf{r}_i - \mathbf{r}_j\|} \quad (1.3)$$

One of its solutions is the ground state electronic wave function determined from the time-independent electronic Schrödinger equation,

$$\hat{\mathcal{H}}_e \phi_e(\mathbf{r}_1, \dots, \mathbf{r}_n; \mathbf{R}_1, \dots, \mathbf{R}_N) = \mathcal{E}_{BO}(\mathbf{R}_1, \dots, \mathbf{R}_N)\phi_e$$
$$\times (\mathbf{r}_1, \dots, \mathbf{r}_n; \mathbf{R}_1, \dots, \mathbf{R}_N) \quad (1.4)$$

The quantity $\mathcal{E}_{BO}(\mathbf{R}_1, \dots, \mathbf{R}_N)$ in Eq. (1.4), called the BO energy, is like a classical potential energy surface that depends only on the position of the nuclei. Solving Eq. (1.4) is a standard task *ab initio* in QM chemistry, which can be performed by using various specialized computer programs [Schmidt *et al.* (1993); Frisch *et al.* (2016); Neese (2012); Shao *et al.* (2015)]. We will not go into how this is done, as it is a very specialized subject that deserves extensive explanations. It is sufficient to say that lately, excellent programs have become available for the determination of the BO energy surface, $\mathcal{E}_{BO}(\mathbf{R}_1, \dots, \mathbf{R}_N)$ for the nuclei.

1.2 Classical dynamics and Ehrenfest theorem

Once the BO energy surface corresponding to the ground state of the electrons is determined, two routes are possible. If we want to account for the QM nature of the nuclei, we express the wave function of the electrons and nuclei in the form,

$$\Psi(\mathbf{R}_1, \dots, \mathbf{R}_N, \mathbf{r}_1, \dots, \mathbf{r}_n, t) = \chi(\mathbf{R}_1, \dots, \mathbf{R}_N, t)$$
$$\times \phi_e(\mathbf{r}_1, \dots, \mathbf{r}_n; \mathbf{R}_1, \dots, \mathbf{R}_N) \quad (1.5)$$

where $\chi(\mathbf{R}_1, \dots, \mathbf{R}_N, t)$ is the time-dependent wave function of the nuclei, and substitute this form in Eq. (1.1). We then find the time-dependent

Schrödinger equation for the nuclei,

$$i\hbar\frac{\partial}{\partial t}\chi(\mathbf{R}_1,\ldots,\mathbf{R}_N,t) = \hat{\mathcal{H}}_{\mathrm{n}}\,\chi(\mathbf{R}_1,\ldots,\mathbf{R}_N,t) \tag{1.6}$$

where

$$\hat{\mathcal{H}}_{\mathrm{n}} = \sum_i \frac{\mathbf{P}_i^2}{2M_i} + \mathcal{E}_{\mathrm{BO}}(\mathbf{R}_1,\ldots,\mathbf{R}_N) \tag{1.7}$$

is the Hamiltonian of the nuclei. To obtain Eq. (1.6), the nucleus–electron cross-term $\mathbf{P}_i^2\phi_{\mathrm{e}}(\mathbf{r}_1,\ldots,\mathbf{r}_n;\mathbf{R}_1,\ldots,\mathbf{R}_N)$ was neglected. This assumes that the dependence of ϕ_{e} on the nuclear coordinates $\mathbf{R}_i$ is weak. This is the adiabatic approximation. Alternatively, we may wish to adopt a pure classical treatment for the nuclei. A critical question is to know when such a classical treatment is valid, and when it is not. Ehrenfest's theorem (1880–1933) states that [Merzbacher (1998)],

$$M_i\frac{d^2\langle\mathbf{R}_i\rangle}{dt^2} = -\langle\boldsymbol{\nabla}_i\mathcal{E}_{\mathrm{BO}}(\mathbf{R}_1,\ldots,\mathbf{R}_N)\rangle \tag{1.8}$$

where the bracket $\langle\ldots\rangle$ represent a QM average using the time-dependent wave function of the nuclei,

$$\langle\ldots\rangle = \int d\mathbf{R}_1\cdots\int d\mathbf{R}_N\,\chi^*(\mathbf{R}_1,\ldots,\mathbf{R}_N,t)\,\ldots\,\chi(\mathbf{R}_1,\ldots,\mathbf{R}_N,t) \tag{1.9}$$

If the nuclei are heavy (heavier than hydrogen) and the temperature is not too low (∼300K), then the wave function is expected to have a narrow peak and the QM-averaged gradient becomes,

$$\langle\boldsymbol{\nabla}_i\mathcal{E}_{\mathrm{BO}}(\mathbf{R}_1,\ldots,\mathbf{R}_N)\rangle \approx \boldsymbol{\nabla}_i\mathcal{E}_{\mathrm{BO}}(\langle\mathbf{R}_1\rangle,\ldots,\langle\mathbf{R}_N\rangle) \tag{1.10}$$

(We replaced the average of a function of variables by the function of the average of those variables.) Under these conditions, a purely classical dynamics expressed in terms of the QM average position of the nuclei:

$$M_i\frac{d^2\langle\mathbf{R}_i\rangle}{dt^2} = -\boldsymbol{\nabla}_i\mathcal{E}_{\mathrm{BO}}(\langle\mathbf{R}_1\rangle,\ldots,\langle\mathbf{R}_N\rangle) \tag{1.11}$$

is a valid and reasonable approximation. The gradient of the potential energy is classically equal to a negative of the force acting on a particle i, $\mathbf{F}_i$, and Eq. (1.11) can be recognized as the familiar classical Newton's equation of motion "$F = MA$" for the QM average positions of the nuclei $\langle\mathbf{R}_i\rangle$.

It should be noted that the classical dynamics of the nuclei described above is still taking place on the BO energy surface $\mathcal{E}_{BO}$ obtained by solving the electronic Hamiltonian. Thus, the influence of quantum mechanics is still present in this model, but it is expressed primarily via the electronic BO energy surface that governs the dynamical motion of the nuclei.

Added note: Demonstrate Ehrenfest's theorem

The time derivative of any operator A is

$$\frac{d}{dt}\langle A \rangle = \frac{1}{i\hbar}\langle [A, \hat{\mathcal{H}}_n]\rangle + \left\langle \frac{\partial A}{\partial t} \right\rangle \tag{1.12}$$

where $[A, \hat{\mathcal{H}}_n] = A\hat{\mathcal{H}}_n - \hat{\mathcal{H}}_n A$, and the time derivative of the QM average position is

$$\frac{d}{dt}\langle \mathbf{R}_i \rangle = \frac{1}{i\hbar}\left\langle \left[\mathbf{R}_i, \hat{\mathcal{H}}_n\right]\right\rangle$$

$$= \frac{1}{i\hbar}\left\langle \left[\mathbf{R}_i, \frac{\mathbf{P}_i^2}{2M_i}\right]\right\rangle$$

$$= \frac{1}{i\hbar}\left\langle \frac{i\hbar\mathbf{P}_i}{M_i}\right\rangle$$

$$= \frac{1}{M_i}\langle \mathbf{P}_i \rangle \tag{1.13}$$

(where $[\mathbf{R}_i, \mathbf{P}_i^2] = 2i\hbar\mathbf{P}_i$ was used) and the time derivative of the QM average momentum is

$$\frac{d}{dt}\langle \mathbf{P}_i \rangle = \frac{1}{i\hbar}\langle [\mathbf{P}_i, \hat{\mathcal{H}}_n]\rangle$$

$$= \frac{1}{i\hbar}\langle [\mathbf{P}_i, \mathcal{E}_{BO}(\mathbf{R}_1, \ldots, \mathbf{R}_N)]\rangle$$

$$= \frac{1}{i\hbar}\langle (-i\hbar)\nabla_i\mathcal{E}_{BO}(\mathbf{R}_1, \ldots, \mathbf{R}_N)\rangle$$

$$= -\langle \nabla_i\mathcal{E}_{BO}(\mathbf{R}_1, \ldots, \mathbf{R}_N)\rangle \tag{1.14}$$

Substituting Eq. (1.13) in Eq. (1.14) yields Eq. (1.8).

In practice, the classical nuclei approximation may still remain fairly accurate, even in the case of light atoms like hydrogen, as long as no chemical bond is formed or broken. Thus, biomolecules comprised of many chemical groups involving hydrogens, for example, hydrocarbons ($-CH$, CH_2, CH_3), hydroxyls ($-OH$), carboxylates ($-COOH$), and amides ($-NH$), can be represented more or less accurately by classical dynamics if they remain chemically intact. On the other hand, proton transfer between different atoms is an important process that is not accurately represented by classical simulations. One simulation method that enables simulation of quantum nuclei effects is called discretized Feynman path integrals, whereby each classical particle is replaced by a small necklace of pseudo-particles (the looseness of the necklace decreases for heavy nuclei). Readers interested in further information on this topic are referred to a more specialized publication [Chandler and Wolynes (1981)].

1.3 The concept of force field

For the sake of computational efficiency, it is reasonable to approximate the quantum mechanical BO potential energy surface by using a force field $U(\mathbf{r}_1, \ldots, \mathbf{r}_N)$ constructed from simple analytical and differentiable functions. (Hereafter, we use the lowercase m_i, $\mathbf{r}_i$, $\mathbf{v}_i$, and $\mathbf{p}_i$ to denote the mass, coordinates, velocity, and momenta of particle i, respectively). In many cases, this can be a very effective approximation [Cornell *et al.* (1995); Jorgensen *et al.* (1996); MacKerell *et al.* (1998)]. For example, if a chemical bond is not expected to break during the simulated period then it is perfectly reasonable to represent this bond with a simple function comprising a single energy minimum at the equilibrium distance, such as a quadratic potential $\propto (b - b_{\mathrm{eq}})^2$. As shown in Figure 1.2, this amounts to perform a Taylor series expansion of $\mathcal{E}_{\mathrm{BO}}$ as a function of the bond length b near the energy minimum b_{eq},

$$\mathcal{E}_{\mathrm{BO}}(b) = \mathcal{E}_{\mathrm{BO}}(b)\Big|_{b_{\mathrm{eq}}} + \frac{1}{2}\mathcal{E}_{\mathrm{BO}}''(b)\Big|_{b_{\mathrm{eq}}} (b - b_{\mathrm{eq}})^2$$

$$= E_{\mathrm{b}} + \frac{1}{2}K^{(\mathrm{bond})}(b - b_{\mathrm{eq}})^2 \tag{1.15}$$

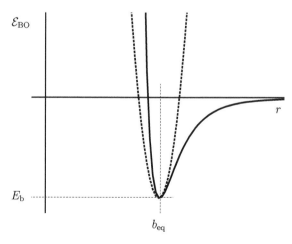

Fig. 1.2   Approximating the potential energy of a chemical bond by a quadratic potential (dashed line) near the energy minimum at b_{eq}.

where $K^{(\text{bond})}$ is the harmonic force constant of the bond, and E_b is an offset constant of no consequence for the molecular mechanical force field because the bond is never allowed to break. A similar functional form can typically be used for the covalent angles between adjacent bonds, $\propto (\theta - \theta_{\text{eq}})^2$. Dihedral angles involving four atoms, which must be periodic over a complete rotation of $360°$, are typically represented by a sum of familiar trigonometric functions such as sine and cosine. These contributions (bonds, angles, and dihedrals) correspond to the so-called covalent or "bonded" energy terms in the force field. Additional contributions arise from the so-called "nonbonded" energy terms, which comprise the core repulsion, van der Waals dispersion, and electrostatic charge-charge interactions. The core repulsion is an essential component, due to the combined effect of electrostatic repulsion of nuclei and Pauli's exclusion principle that prevents the electron clouds of each atom from overlapping significantly. The attractive van der Waals dispersion, going as $-B/R^6$, is the manifestation of a QM effect arising from the correlated fluctuations of the electron clouds of two atoms. According to the QM perturbation theory, the van der Waals dispersion interaction between two particles is also related to their polarizability coefficient (see below).

As an example of biomolecular modeling, let us consider a short polypeptide with a water molecule as depicted in Figure 1.3. In this case, we want to approximate the QM potential energy surface $\mathcal{E}_{\text{BO}}$ via the force field U. The various elements of the molecular mechanical force field are

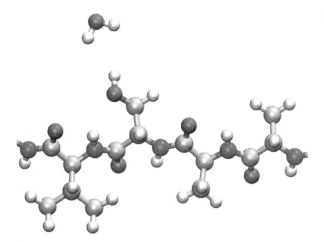

Fig. 1.3 Illustration of a polypeptide fragment with a water molecule. The sequence (reading from right to left) is -Ala-Ala-Ser-Val-. The figure was prepared using the program VMD [Humphrey *et al.* (1996)].

illustrated schematically in Eq. (1.16).

$$U(\mathbf{r}_1,\ldots,\mathbf{r}_N) = \sum_{\text{all bonds}} \frac{1}{2} K_i^{(\text{bond})} (b_i - b_{\text{eq},i})^2$$

$$+ \sum_{\text{all angles}} \frac{1}{2} K_i^{(\text{angle})} (\theta_i - \theta_{\text{eq},i})^2$$

$$+ \sum_{\text{all dihedrals}} \sum_i K_i^{(\text{dihedral})} \cos(m_i \phi_i)$$

$$+ \sum_{\text{all nonbonded pairs}} \left(\frac{q_i q_j}{\epsilon r_{ij}} \right.$$

$$\left. + 4\epsilon_{ij} \left[\left(\frac{\sigma_{ij}}{r_{ij}} \right)^{12} - \left(\frac{\sigma_{ij}}{r_{ij}} \right)^6 \right] \right)$$

(1.16)

The bonded or internal covalent terms include chemical bonds, angles, and dihedrals. The nonbonded terms typically include core repulsion, van der Waals dispersive attraction, and charge-charge electrostatic interactions. Typically, nonbonded interactions are not included between atoms that are separated by only one or two chemical bonds. Many simple force fields simply ascribe a partial charge to the atoms (or specific interaction sites within a molecule) as in Eq. (1.16). If those charges are fixed and not allowed to change, the force field is then described as additive or nonpolarizable. This is obviously an approximation because it is expected that the charge distribution of an atom or a molecule will be affected if it is submitted to an external electric field. This is the effect of induced polarization (see below).

In Eq. (1.16), the core repulsion and van der Waals dispersion are conveniently combined into the simple Lennard-Jones (LJ) 12-6 potential, $u_{\text{LJ}}(r) = 4\epsilon_{ij} \left[(\sigma_{ij}/r)^{12} - (\sigma_{ij}/r)^6 \right]$, where r is the distance between the particles i and j. Introduced by John Lennard-Jones in 1924, the functional form of the LJ was chosen because the inverse powers 6 and 12 of the distance were directly related, with $r^6 = (r^2 \times r^2 \times r^2)$, and $r^{12} = (r^6 \times r^6)$, which enabled a rapid and efficient numerical approximation. Thus, while the attractive function $-(4\epsilon_{ij}\sigma_{ij}^6)/r^6$ has the expected form for the van der Waals dispersion at large distance, no special physical meaning should be ascribed to the $1/r^{12}$ core repulsion part of the LJ potential.

The functional form of the LJ potential is such that specific parameters are needed for all pairs i and j, ϵ_{ij} and σ_{ij}. In principle, one would want to determine the optimal value of all those parameters, but this is difficult. For the sake of expediency, the Lorentz–Berteloot combination rules are commonly used to generate the parameters: $\sigma_{ij} = \frac{1}{2}\sigma_{ii} + \frac{1}{2}\sigma_{jj}$ (arithmetic combination) and $\epsilon_{ij} = \sqrt{\epsilon_i \epsilon_j}$ (geometric combination). The parameter σ_{ij} represents the size of the core repulsive sphere (see Figure 1.4). As illustrated in Figure 1.5, if each particle is a hard sphere, then the smallest possible distance between the two particles would be equal to the sum of their respective radii, which provides an intuitive explanation for the arithmetic combination rule to generate the parameter σ_{ij}. The parameter ϵ_{ij} represents the depth of the well associated with the van der Waals dispersion interaction. As explained below, the dispersion interaction is related to atomic polarizabilities, which partly justifies the use of geometric combination rule to generate this parameter.

Equation (1.16) summarizes the components of a nonpolarizable additive force field. To go beyond this simple approximation, it is necessary to account for induced polarization. Classically, the dipole $\delta\boldsymbol{\mu}$ that is induced in response to the applied field is given by $\alpha\mathbf{E}$, where the constant α is the polarizability coefficient of the atom. This situation is illustrated schematically in Figure 1.6. To clarify the physics underlying induced polarization, let us consider the Hamiltonian of an atom placed in an external electric field $\mathbf{E}$, $\hat{\mathcal{H}} = \hat{\mathcal{H}}_0 - \delta\boldsymbol{\mu}\cdot\mathbf{E}$, where $\hat{\mathcal{H}}_0$ is the unperturbed Hamiltonian, and $\delta\boldsymbol{\mu}$

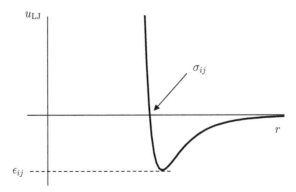

Fig. 1.4 Illustration of the LJ 6-12 potential. The depth of the van der Waals attraction is equal to $-\epsilon_{ij}$ and the sharp repulsion starts at a distance of σ_{ij} (the actual minimum is located at $2^{1/6}\sigma_{ij}$).

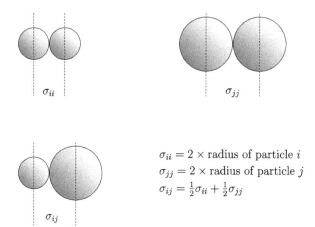

$$\sigma_{ii} = 2 \times \text{radius of particle } i$$
$$\sigma_{jj} = 2 \times \text{radius of particle } j$$
$$\sigma_{ij} = \tfrac{1}{2}\sigma_{ii} + \tfrac{1}{2}\sigma_{jj}$$

Fig. 1.5 Illustration of the combination rule for the effective LJ radius of two atoms, σ_{ij}. If the particles were pictured as hard spheres then the sharp repulsion between them would start at a distance equal to the sum of their radii.

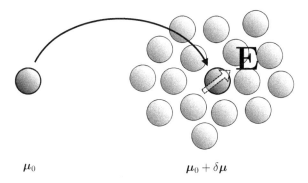

$\boldsymbol{\mu}_0$ $\qquad\qquad\qquad\qquad\qquad$ $\boldsymbol{\mu}_0 + \delta\boldsymbol{\mu}$

Fig. 1.6 Schematic representation of the polarization induced in a particle by the electric field arising from the surrounding atoms. The dipole of an isolated atom in vacuum is $\boldsymbol{\mu}_0$, and the total dipole after induction is $\boldsymbol{\mu}_0 + \delta\boldsymbol{\mu}$.

is the induced electric dipole moment of the atom. According to Rayleigh–Schrödinger perturbation theory, the dipole induced by an external electric field in a spherically symmetric atom is [Merzbacher (1998)],

$$
\begin{aligned}
\langle \delta\boldsymbol{\mu} \rangle &= 2 \sum_{n>0} \frac{\langle \phi_0 | \delta\boldsymbol{\mu} | \phi_n \rangle \langle \phi_n | (-\delta\boldsymbol{\mu} \cdot \mathbf{E}) | \phi_0 \rangle}{\epsilon_0 - \epsilon_n} \\
&= -\frac{2}{3} \frac{\langle \delta\boldsymbol{\mu} \cdot \delta\boldsymbol{\mu} \rangle_0}{\Delta\epsilon} \mathbf{E} \\
&= \alpha \, \mathbf{E}
\end{aligned}
\tag{1.17}
$$

Here, ϕ_0 is the BO electronic ground state of the atom under consideration, ϕ_n is the BO nth excited state, and $\Delta\epsilon$ is the effective energy gap between the ground state and excited states of the atom. Thus, the polarizability coefficient α is equal to $(\frac{2}{3})\langle\delta\boldsymbol{\mu}\cdot\delta\boldsymbol{\mu}\rangle_0/\Delta\epsilon$, and is shown to be related to the quadratic quantum fluctuations of the dipole moment.

Interestingly, the dispersive van der Waals interactions between two atoms are closely related to the polarizability coefficient α. Let us consider a Hamiltonian of two atoms a and b placed at some distance from one another, $\hat{\mathcal{H}} = \hat{\mathcal{H}}_0^a - \hat{\mathcal{H}}_0^b + \delta\boldsymbol{\mu}^a \cdot \mathbf{T} \cdot \delta\boldsymbol{\mu}^b$, where $\mathbf{T}$ is the dipole-dipole tensor that depends on the relative position $\mathbf{r}$ of the two atoms, $3(\hat{\mathbf{r}} : \hat{\mathbf{r}} - \mathbf{I})/r^3$. According to Rayleigh–Schrödinger perturbation theory, again, the energy is to second order,

$$
\begin{aligned}
E_{\text{dis}} &= \sum_{n>0} \frac{||\langle\phi_0^a\phi_0^b|(\delta\boldsymbol{\mu}^a \cdot \mathbf{T} \cdot \delta\boldsymbol{\mu}^b)|\phi_n^a\phi_n^b\rangle||^2}{\epsilon_0 - \epsilon_n} \\
&\approx -\frac{\langle(\delta\boldsymbol{\mu}^a \cdot \mathbf{T} \cdot \delta\boldsymbol{\mu}^b)^2\rangle_0}{\Delta\epsilon^a + \Delta\epsilon^b} \\
&\approx -\frac{3}{2}\left(\frac{\alpha^a \, \alpha^b}{r^6}\right)\left(\frac{\Delta\epsilon^a \Delta\epsilon^b}{\Delta\epsilon^a + \Delta\epsilon^b}\right)
\end{aligned}
\tag{1.18}
$$

where $\Delta\epsilon^a$ and $\Delta\epsilon^b$ are the effective electronic excitation energy of atom a and b. If the two atoms are identical, the coefficient of the dispersive term is $-3\alpha^2\Delta\epsilon/4$. This development shows how the magnitude of the dispersive van der Waals interactions between two atoms is closely related to the product of the polarizability coefficients of these atoms. Both terms account for the response of the electric wave function when the nuclei are changing their position.

Effective force fields that do not explicitly account for induced polarization may be constructed and optimized to be consistent with this approximation. However, the existence of induced polarization leads to an important observation that can be illustrated with the simple example shown in Figure 1.6. The dipole of the isolated atom in vacuum is $\boldsymbol{\mu}_0$, and the total dipole after induction in the polarizing environment is $\boldsymbol{\mu}_0 + \delta\boldsymbol{\mu}$. Classically, the total energy of the atom in the polarizing environment is,

$$
U_{\text{pol}}(\delta\boldsymbol{\mu}) = \frac{1}{2\alpha}(\delta\boldsymbol{\mu}\cdot\delta\boldsymbol{\mu}) - (\boldsymbol{\mu}_0 + \delta\boldsymbol{\mu})\cdot\mathbf{E}
\tag{1.19}
$$

where the first term represents the unfavorable energy for inducing a dipole $\delta\boldsymbol{\mu}$ (i.e., distorting the electronic distribution). The value of $\delta\boldsymbol{\mu}$ is determined by finding the minimum of the total energy U_{pol},

$$\frac{\partial}{\partial(\delta\boldsymbol{\mu})}U_{\text{pol}}(\delta\boldsymbol{\mu}) = 0$$

$$= \frac{\delta\boldsymbol{\mu}}{\alpha} - \mathbf{E} \qquad (1.20)$$

Substituting the induced dipole, $\delta\boldsymbol{\mu} = \alpha\mathbf{E}$, in the total energy yields,

$$U_{\text{pol}} = -\boldsymbol{\mu}_0 \cdot \mathbf{E} - \frac{1}{2}\delta\boldsymbol{\mu} \cdot \mathbf{E}$$

$$= -\left(\boldsymbol{\mu}_0 + \frac{1}{2}\delta\boldsymbol{\mu}\right) \cdot \mathbf{E} \qquad (1.21)$$

Clearly, to reproduce the same energy with a fixed dipole in a nonpolarizable (additive) force field, $U_{\text{pol}} = -\boldsymbol{\mu}_{\text{fixed}} \cdot \mathbf{E}$, one needs to have,

$$\boldsymbol{\mu}_{\text{fixed}} = \boldsymbol{\mu}_0 + \frac{1}{2}\delta\boldsymbol{\mu} \qquad (1.22)$$

This result has important consequences for the physical significance of the electrostatic fields determined from models that do not explicitly account for induced polarization. For example, the electric dipole moment of an isolated water molecule in vacuum is about 1.85 Debye (D). *Ab initio* simulations indicate that the dipole increases to about 3.0 D in the condensed liquid phase. The induced contribution $\delta\boldsymbol{\mu}$ is thus, $3.0 - 1.85 = 1.15$ D. According to Eq. (1.22), the optimal fixed dipole required to reproduce the total energy is 2.43 D. This value is close to the empirically optimized electrical dipole moment of 2.35 D for nonpolarizable models of water [Jorgensen *et al.* (1983); Berendsen *et al.* (1981)]. In conclusion, while the nonpolarizable force fields may yield an effective approximation to the BO energy surface of acceptable accuracy, it is important to keep in mind they are not designed to represent the true electric fields and induced dipoles in the system.

1.4 Molecular dynamics simulations

Having described the microscopic forces between atoms in terms of the BO energy surface and explained the concept of force field, it is interesting to conclude this chapter with an introduction to an important technique called molecular dynamics (MD) simulation. MD consists of generating a classical trajectory of a detailed atomic system by integrating Newton's equation of motion "$F = MA$" numerically. The trajectory then takes the form of a sequence of discrete positions for all the atoms, $\{\mathbf{r}_i(0), \mathbf{r}_i(\Delta t), \mathbf{r}_i(2\Delta t), \dots\}$, where Δt is a small time-step [Alder and Wainwright (1959); Rahman (1964); Stillinger and Rahman (1974); McCammon *et al.* (1977)]. The result is literally a "simulation" of the motions of all the atoms as a function of time. To obtain a numerical algorithm enabling the propagation of the system, let us consider the Taylor series of the classical trajectory for atom i during a time t, forward and backward in time. We get:

$$\mathbf{r}_i(t + \Delta t) = \mathbf{r}_i(t) + \dot{\mathbf{r}}_i(t)\Delta t + \frac{1}{2}\ddot{\mathbf{r}}_i(t)\Delta t^2 + \frac{1}{3!}\dddot{\mathbf{r}}_i(t)\Delta t^3 + \cdots \quad (1.23)$$

and

$$\mathbf{r}_i(t - \Delta t) = \mathbf{r}_i(t) - \dot{\mathbf{r}}_i(t)\Delta t + \frac{1}{2}\ddot{\mathbf{r}}_i(t)\Delta t^2 - \frac{1}{3!}\dddot{\mathbf{r}}_i(t)\Delta t^3 + \cdots \quad (1.24)$$

If we add the two lines, we get:

$$\mathbf{r}_i(t + \Delta t) = 2\mathbf{r}_i(t) - \mathbf{r}_i(t - \Delta t) + \ddot{\mathbf{r}}_i(t)\Delta t^2 \quad (1.25)$$

where we have dropped out the terms in fourth order in Δt and higher. We then use the microscopic force $\mathbf{F}_i(t) = m_i\ddot{\mathbf{r}}_i(t)$ to write,

$$\mathbf{r}_i(t + \Delta t) = 2\mathbf{r}_i(t) - \mathbf{r}_i(t - \Delta t) + \frac{\mathbf{F}_i(t)}{m_i}\Delta t^2 \quad (1.26)$$

This equation for the propagation of the classical trajectory is called the Verlet algorithm [Verlet (1967)]. One attractive feature of Eq. (1.26) is that the force calculation, which is by far the most computationally extensive component of MD, is needed only once per time-step. The velocities are not required explicitly for propagation in Eq. (1.26), but they can be calculated on the half time-step by considering the finite difference,

$$\mathbf{v}_i\left(t + \frac{\Delta t}{2}\right) = \frac{\mathbf{r}_i(t + \Delta t) - \mathbf{r}_i(t)}{\Delta t} \quad (1.27)$$

Velocities are needed to monitor the temperature during the simulation (see below). For practical calculations, one simply propagates the system by looping over Eq. (1.26) and thus calculating the position of each the atom at its next time-step based on the total force that it experiences. This procedure is repeated to generate the classical trajectory of all dynamical variables at discrete times t_k, $\{\mathbf{r}_1(t_k), \dots, \mathbf{r}_N(t_k), \mathbf{v}_1(t_k), \dots, \mathbf{v}_N(t_k)\}$, with $k = 1, 2, \ldots$. The temperature T of the system in absolute Kelvin is calculated from the kinetic energy as,

$$T = \frac{2}{3Nk_{\mathrm{B}}} \sum_{i=1}^{N} \frac{1}{2} m_i (\mathbf{v}_i)^2 \tag{1.28}$$

where $k_{\mathrm{B}} = 1.38 \times 10^{-23}$ Joule/K is the Boltzmann constant (see Eq. (2.19) in Chapter 2). Assuming that a trajectory of length $\mathcal{T}$ is sufficiently long to sample all the relevant states of the system in a manner that is consistent with thermodynamic equilibrium, averages of observable A may then be calculated from time-average:

$$\overline{A} = \frac{1}{\mathcal{T}} \int_0^{\mathcal{T}} A(t') dt'$$

$$= \frac{1}{M} \sum_{k=1}^{M} A(t_k) \tag{1.29}$$

The first MD simulation of a small protein was published almost 50 years ago [McCammon *et al.* (1977)]. With the availability of atomic force fields, simulation methodologies have now reached the point where one can generate classical trajectories of realistic models of very large and complex biomolecular systems [Phillips *et al.* (2005); Hess *et al.* (2008); Brooks *et al.* (2009); Shaw *et al.* (2010); Gotz *et al.* (2012); Eastman *et al.* (2013)]. Such trajectories, though an approximation to the real world, provide detailed information about the time course of the atomic motions, which is impossible to access experimentally.

Chapter 2

Equilibrium statistical mechanics

To provide a complete classical description of an atomic system, we need to specify the position $\mathbf{r}_i$ and momenta $\mathbf{p}_i$ of all the atoms. But in practice, when we probe a molecular system experimentally, we do not have access to all this information. In fact, even in the case of computer simulations where we have access to all this information, we may still wish to account for the behavior of the system via a reduced set of key variables. Statistical mechanics is a powerful theoretical framework that allows us to achieve a rational management of the limited information about these systems. For this reason, it is the language of choice when trying to communicate about complex molecular systems.

2.1 Energy conservation in classical mechanics

To formulate the basic concepts of statistical mechanics of classical systems, let us first define the Hamiltonian,

$$\mathcal{H} = \sum_i \frac{\mathbf{p}_i^2}{2m_i} + U(\mathbf{r}_1, \ldots, \mathbf{r}_N) \tag{2.1}$$

where the first term is the kinetic energy, and the second term is the potential energy. In the absence of dissipative forces and external time-dependent perturbation, the Hamiltonian $\mathcal{H}$ is equal to the total energy E_{tot}. It is a conserved quantity, which means that it is not changing with time. This is easily demonstrated by considering the time derivative of $\mathcal{H}$,

$$\frac{d\mathcal{H}}{dt} = \sum_i \frac{d\mathbf{p}_i}{dt} \cdot \frac{\mathbf{p}_i}{m_i} + \sum_i \boldsymbol{\nabla}_i U(\mathbf{r}_1, \ldots, \mathbf{r}_N) \cdot \frac{d\mathbf{r}_i}{dt}$$

$$= \sum_i \left(m_i \frac{d^2 \mathbf{r}_i}{dt^2} + \boldsymbol{\nabla}_i U(\mathbf{r}_1, \ldots, \mathbf{r}_N) \right) \cdot \frac{d\mathbf{r}_i}{dt}$$

$$= 0 \tag{2.2}$$

If a system evolves according to Newton's classical equation of motion, then

$$m_i \frac{d^2 \mathbf{r}_i}{dt^2} = -\boldsymbol{\nabla}_i U(\mathbf{r}_1, \ldots, \mathbf{r}_N) \tag{2.3}$$

The implication is that the total energy E_{tot} of an isolated system (kinetic plus potential) is conserved.

2.2   Microstates and phase space

Obviously, there are many ways for a system to have a given total energy E_{tot}. The complete specification of the status of a classical system (coordinates and momenta) is typically denoted as a point in phase space,

$$\boldsymbol{\Gamma} \equiv \{\mathbf{r}_1, \ldots, \mathbf{r}_N, \mathbf{p}_1, \ldots, , \mathbf{p}_N\} \tag{2.4}$$

Dividing the entire phase space in small volume elements Δv, each element represents a "microstate" of the system. Given the total energy of a system, the total "number of accessible microstates" may be written as

$$\Omega(E_{\text{tot}}) \equiv \frac{1}{\Delta v} \int d\boldsymbol{\Gamma} \, \delta\Big[\mathcal{H}(\boldsymbol{\Gamma}) - E_{\text{tot}}\Big] \tag{2.5}$$

Quantum mechanics tells us that Δv is on the order of h^{3N}, where h is Planck's constant, but this will not have an immediate impact on the following considerations.

Typically, the number of microstates of a large system is expected to grow sharply when the total energy E_{tot} is increasing. Conversely, very few microstates are accessible when the energy is close to a minimum. At the absolute minimum, there might be a single possible microstate that is allowed. Without further knowledge about a system, it makes sense to assume that all the microstates that satisfy the condition $\mathcal{H} = E_{\text{tot}}$ are all equiprobable with the same statistical weights. However, if we have additional information, for example, to label the microstates, then the marginal probability of picking a specific label will depend on the fraction of microstates that carry that label. In Section 2.3, we will exploit this concept to formulate the probability of the microstates of a small subsystem that is in contact with a heat bath.

2.3 The Maxwell–Boltzmann equilibrium distribution

Let us consider a system comprising a small subsystem embedded into a much larger heat bath. The volume V of the subsystem and the number of particles N that it contains are fixed. We refer to the subsystem together with the heat bath as the combined system. While heat energy can be exchanged between the subsystem and the surrounding bath, the total energy of the combined system E_{tot} is constant. This arrangement is illustrated in Figure 2.1. The total energy is E_{tot}. Without additional information, all the microstates of the combined system (subsystem plus heat bath) are equiprobable. However, we can also label the microstates of the combined system according to the specific microstate $\mathbf{\Gamma}$ of the small subsystem with a specific value of the total energy, $\mathcal{H}(\mathbf{\Gamma})$. Consequently, the remainder of the outer system (the heat bath) must have energy $E_{tot} - \mathcal{H}(\mathbf{\Gamma})$.

If all the microstates of the large combined system are equiprobable, then the probability to find the subsystem in the microstate $\mathbf{\Gamma}$ should be proportional to the fraction of microstates of the heat bath consistent with

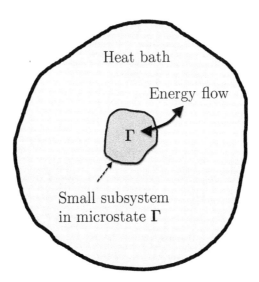

Fig. 2.1 Illustration of an isolated system comprising a small subsystem embedded into an extremely large heat bath. The volume V of the subsystem and the number of particles N that it contains are fixed. The total energy of the combined system (the small subsystem plus the surrounding heat bath) is constant, $E_{tot} = $ constant, but heat (energy) can be exchanged between the subsystem and the surrounding bath. The microstate $\mathbf{\Gamma}$ of the subsystem is used to label the status of the combined system.

this situation,

$$P(\mathbf{\Gamma}) \propto \Omega(E_{\text{tot}} - \mathcal{H}(\mathbf{\Gamma}))$$

$$\propto e^{\ln[\Omega(E_{\text{tot}} - \mathcal{H}(\mathbf{\Gamma}))]} \tag{2.6}$$

We then expand the argument of the exponential in terms of a Taylor–McLaurin series:

$$\ln[\Omega(E_{\text{tot}} - \mathcal{H}(\mathbf{\Gamma}))] \approx \ln[\Omega(E_{\text{tot}})] - \frac{\partial \ln \Omega(E)}{\partial E}\bigg|_{(E=E_{\text{tot}})} \mathcal{H}(\mathbf{\Gamma})$$

$$= \ln[\Omega(E_{\text{tot}})] - \beta\mathcal{H}(\mathbf{\Gamma}) \tag{2.7}$$

where β is a constant parameter that is a property of the bath. We can identify the constant β by relating this analysis to the properties of an ideal gas. For example, the internal energy of an ideal gas of N particles is equal to the average kinetic energy K,

$$K = \left\langle \sum_i \frac{\mathbf{p}_i^2}{2m_i} \right\rangle \tag{2.8}$$

$$= \sum_i \frac{\langle \mathbf{p}_i^2 \rangle}{2m_i} \tag{2.9}$$

$$= \frac{3N}{2\beta} \tag{2.10}$$

where

$$\langle \mathbf{p}_i^2 \rangle = \frac{\int d\mathbf{p}_i \ (\mathbf{p}_i^2/2m_i) \ e^{-\beta \mathbf{p}_i^2/2m_i}}{\int d\mathbf{p}_i \ e^{-\beta \mathbf{p}_i^2/2m_i}} \tag{2.11}$$

has been used. It is known that the internal energy of the ideal gas is

$$K = \frac{3}{2}nRT \tag{2.12}$$

where n is the number of moles and R is the universal gas constant. The number of particles is $N = n\mathcal{N}_{\text{A}}$, where $\mathcal{N}_{\text{A}}$ is Avogadro's number (6.022×10^{23}). The internal energy of the gas is $(3/2)Nk_{\text{B}}T$, with $R = k_{\text{B}}\mathcal{N}_{\text{A}}$, where k_{B} is the Boltzmann constant equal to 1.38×10^{-23} J/K. Thus, by this equivalence, we find that $\beta \equiv 1/k_{\text{B}}T$.

Having identified β, we can now write the probability of the subsystem in contact with a heat bath at temperature T of being in microstate $\mathbf{\Gamma}$ as

$$P(\mathbf{\Gamma}) \propto e^{-\mathcal{H}(\mathbf{\Gamma})/k_{\text{B}}T} \tag{2.13}$$

This is called the canonical distribution. The quantity, $e^{-E/k_B T}$, is commonly referred to as the "Boltzmann factor." Of course, probabilities need to be normalized, which implies that the sum over all possible microstates must be equal to 1,

$$P(\mathbf{\Gamma}) = \frac{e^{-\mathcal{H}(\mathbf{\Gamma})/k_B T}}{\int d\mathbf{\Gamma}\, e^{-\mathcal{H}(\mathbf{\Gamma})/k_B T}} \qquad (2.14)$$

We write the average of an observable A as,

$$\langle A \rangle = \frac{\int d\mathbf{\Gamma}\, A\, e^{-\mathcal{H}(\mathbf{\Gamma})/k_B T}}{\int d\mathbf{\Gamma}\, e^{-\mathcal{H}(\mathbf{\Gamma})/k_B T}} \qquad (2.15)$$

While such averages may sometimes be evaluated explicitly in closed form for some special cases, see Eqs. (2.19) and (2.20) below, more commonly they are calculated from equilibrium simulations according to Eq. (1.29) or one of the sampling algorithms discussed in Chapter 12.

Because the total energy is a sum of kinetic and potential energy, the canonical distribution can be factored as a product of two distributions involving, respectively, the momenta and the coordinates,

$$P(\mathbf{\Gamma}) = P_M(\mathbf{p}_1) \dots P_M(\mathbf{p}_N) P_B(\mathbf{r}_1, \dots, \mathbf{r}_N) \qquad (2.16)$$

where $P_M(\mathbf{p}_i)$ is the Maxwell distribution:

$$P_M(\mathbf{p}_i) = \frac{e^{-\mathbf{p}_i^2/2m_i k_B T}}{\int d\mathbf{p}_i\, e^{-\mathbf{p}_i^2/2m_i k_B T}} \qquad (2.17)$$

and the Boltzmann configurational probability is

$$P_B(\mathbf{r}_1, \dots, \mathbf{r}_N) = \frac{e^{-U(\mathbf{r}_1, \dots, \mathbf{r}_N)/k_B T}}{\int d\mathbf{r}_1 \cdots \int d\mathbf{r}_N\, e^{-U(\mathbf{r}_1, \dots, \mathbf{r}_N)/k_B T}} \qquad (2.18)$$

This is the statistical distribution for the canonical ensemble, which corresponds to a subsystem of constant volume and constant number of particles. In chemistry, we typically consider a subsystem of variable volume embedded in a heat bath, which leads to an isobaric–isothermal ensemble (constant pressure and constant temperature). We could also consider an open subsystem, allowing the exchange of particles, which leads to a grand canonical ensemble. In the following, we will primarily work from the canonical ensemble at constant temperature and constant volume for the sake of simplicity, and will write P_B as P.

Added note: Equipartition theorem

The statistical distribution of the momenta is a simple Gaussian function. The mean square momentum along the x-direction for a particle of mass m is equal to

$$\langle p_x^2 \rangle = \frac{\int dp_x \, p_x^2 \, e^{-p_x^2/2mk_{\mathrm{B}}T}}{\int dp_x \, e^{-p_x^2/2mk_{\mathrm{B}}T}}$$

$$= mk_{\mathrm{B}}T \tag{2.19}$$

The mean square fluctuation of a particle in a harmonic potential is

$$\langle x^2 \rangle = \frac{\int dx \, x^2 \, e^{-Kx^2/2k_{\mathrm{B}}T}}{\int dx \, e^{-Kx^2/2k_{\mathrm{B}}T}}$$

$$= \frac{k_{\mathrm{B}}T}{K} \tag{2.20}$$

These are manifestations of the so-called equipartition theorem of energy.

Because the kinetic and configurational parts are independent in the canonical distribution, statistical mechanical expressions concerning only atomic positions can formally be developed without explicit attention to the momenta. As such, the distribution of velocities has no impact on the structural averages of an equilibrium system.

2.4   Treatment of a small perturbation

It is often useful to consider the effect of small perturbations on a reference system. Let us assume that the Hamiltonian $\mathcal{H}$ has the form $\mathcal{H}_0 + \alpha A$, where $\mathcal{H}_0$ is the Hamiltonian of a reference system, and αA is a small perturbation. The average of an observable B is expressed as

$$\langle B \rangle = \frac{\int d\boldsymbol{\Gamma} \, B \, e^{-\mathcal{H}(\boldsymbol{\Gamma})/k_{\mathrm{B}}T}}{\int d\boldsymbol{\Gamma} \, e^{-\mathcal{H}(\boldsymbol{\Gamma})/k_{\mathrm{B}}T}} \tag{2.21}$$

We can express the average of B in the perturbed system $\mathcal{H}(\alpha) = \mathcal{H}_0 + \alpha A$:

$$\langle B \rangle_\alpha = \frac{\int d\boldsymbol{\Gamma} \, B \, e^{-\mathcal{H}(\alpha)/k_{\mathrm{B}}T}}{\int d\boldsymbol{\Gamma} \, e^{-\mathcal{H}(\alpha)/k_{\mathrm{B}}T}} \tag{2.22}$$

in terms of average quantities of the reference system with $\alpha = 0$. Let us express the average $\langle B \rangle_\alpha$ in terms of a Taylor series,

$$\langle B \rangle_\alpha = \langle B \rangle_0 + \left. \frac{\partial \langle B \rangle_\alpha}{\partial \alpha} \right|_{\alpha=0} \alpha + \cdots \tag{2.23}$$

where

$$\langle B \rangle_0 = \frac{\int d\Gamma \, B \, e^{-\mathcal{H}_0/k_B T}}{\int d\Gamma \, e^{-\mathcal{H}_0/k_B T}} \tag{2.24}$$

and

$$
\begin{aligned}
\left. \frac{\partial \langle B \rangle_\alpha}{\partial \alpha} \right|_{\alpha=0} &= \left. \frac{\partial}{\partial \alpha} \left(\frac{\int d\Gamma \, B \, e^{-\mathcal{H}(\alpha)/k_B T}}{\int d\Gamma \, e^{-\mathcal{H}(\alpha)/k_B T}} \right) \right|_{\alpha=0} \\[2mm]
&= \left(\frac{\int d\Gamma \, B \, \frac{\partial}{\partial \alpha} e^{-\mathcal{H}(\alpha)/k_B T}}{\int d\Gamma \, e^{-\mathcal{H}(\alpha)/k_B T}} \right. \\[2mm]
&\qquad \left. - \frac{\int d\Gamma \, B \, e^{-\mathcal{H}(\alpha)/k_B T}}{\int d\Gamma \, e^{-\mathcal{H}(\alpha)/k_B T}} \, \frac{\int d\Gamma \, \frac{\partial}{\partial \alpha} e^{-\mathcal{H}(\alpha)/k_B T}}{\int d\Gamma \, e^{-\mathcal{H}(\alpha)/k_B T}} \right) \Bigg|_{\alpha=0} \\[2mm]
&= \left(\frac{\int d\Gamma \, B \left(\frac{-A}{k_B T} \right) e^{-\mathcal{H}(\alpha)/k_B T}}{\int d\Gamma \, e^{-\mathcal{H}(\alpha)/k_B T}} \right. \\[2mm]
&\qquad \left. - \frac{\int d\Gamma \, B \, e^{-\mathcal{H}(\alpha)/k_B T}}{\int d\Gamma \, e^{-\mathcal{H}(\alpha)/k_B T}} \, \frac{\int d\Gamma \left(\frac{-A}{k_B T} \right) e^{-\mathcal{H}(\alpha)/k_B T}}{\int d\Gamma \, e^{-\mathcal{H}(\alpha)/k_B T}} \right) \Bigg|_{\alpha=0} \\[2mm]
&= -\frac{1}{k_B T} \Big(\langle BA \rangle_0 - \langle B \rangle_0 \langle A \rangle_0 \Big) \\[2mm]
&= -\frac{1}{k_B T} \langle \delta B \, \delta A \rangle_0 \tag{2.25}
\end{aligned}
$$

where

$$\delta B = B - \langle B \rangle_0 \tag{2.26}$$

and

$$\delta A = A - \langle A \rangle_0 \tag{2.27}$$

correspond to the deviations of A and B away from their averages in the absence of any perturbation. The subscript 0 means that the averages are calculated in the reference system with Hamiltonian $\mathcal{H}_0$. It follows that, to the first order in α, the average of B is,

$$\langle B \rangle_\alpha = \langle B \rangle_0 - \frac{\alpha}{k_B T} \langle \delta A \, \delta B \rangle_0 \tag{2.28}$$

As an illustration, let us consider the perturbation, $\alpha A = -F x$, caused by the constant force F. To first order in the perturbation, the average deviation of x for the perturbed system is,

$$\langle \delta x \rangle_F = \frac{F}{k_B T} \langle \delta x^2 \rangle_0 \qquad (2.29)$$

By analogy with a simple harmonic system, it is interesting to express the average deviation as, F/K_{eff}, with the effective spring constant $K_{\text{eff}} = k_B T / \langle \delta x^2 \rangle_0$. This general form, involving an effective spring constant that is inversely proportional to the spontaneously quadratic fluctuations of the dynamical variable of interest, arises in a wide variety of situations associated with the linear response of a dynamical system.

This analysis shows that the response of an observable B in a perturbed system typically depends on a quantity,

$$C_{AB} = \langle \delta A \, \delta B \rangle_0 \qquad (2.30)$$

calculated in the unperturbed reference system. C_{AB} is the correlation coefficient between the deviations δA and δB. It is of interest to clarify the significance of correlation coefficients by considering two extreme cases. For example, if δA and δB are statistically independent, then

$$C_{AB} = \langle \delta A \, \delta B \rangle$$
$$= \langle \delta A \rangle \langle \delta B \rangle$$
$$= 0 \qquad (2.31)$$

The correlation coefficient is zero. In contrast, if δA and δB are linearly related, for example, $\delta B = \lambda \delta A$, then the correlation coefficient is tightly constrained. The outcome is displayed more explicitly by considering the normalized correlation coefficient,

$$\overline{C}_{AB} = \frac{\langle \delta A \, \delta B \rangle}{\sqrt{\langle (\delta A)^2 \rangle \langle (\delta B)^2 \rangle}}$$
$$= \frac{\lambda \langle (\delta A)^2 \rangle}{\sqrt{\lambda^2 \langle (\delta A)^2 \rangle}}$$
$$= \text{sign}(\lambda) \qquad (2.32)$$

In this case, regardless of the exact value of λ, the normalized correlation coefficient $\overline{C}_{AB}$ will be equal to either $+1$ or -1, depending on the sign of λ.

These limits also reflect the maximum correlation that can be observed, such that $-1 \leq \overline{C}_{AB} \leq 1$.

In ending this section, it is useful to note that a similar treatment can also be used to determine the derivative of an average observable B with respect to some parameter p,

$$\frac{\partial}{\partial p}\langle B \rangle = \left\langle \frac{\partial B}{\partial p} \right\rangle - \frac{1}{k_B T}\left(\left\langle \frac{\partial B}{\partial p}\frac{\partial U}{\partial p} \right\rangle - \left\langle \frac{\partial B}{\partial p} \right\rangle\left\langle \frac{\partial U}{\partial p} \right\rangle \right) \quad (2.33)$$

This type of expression for the analytical derivative of the average observable $\langle B \rangle$ can be very helpful in systematic efforts dedicated at refining the parameters of a force field to match target experimental values.

2.5 Marginal distribution and the potential of mean force

Let us express the potential energy of a molecular system of N particles as $U(\mathbf{r}_1,\ldots,\mathbf{r}_N) = U(x,\mathbf{Y})$, where x represents a certain degree of freedom, such as the Cartesian coordinate x of a tagged atom, and $\mathbf{Y}$ represents all the remaining degrees of freedom. The configurational probability distribution for all the coordinates is

$$P(x,\mathbf{Y}) = \frac{e^{-U(x,\mathbf{Y})/k_B T}}{\int dx' \int d\mathbf{Y'}\ e^{-U(x',\mathbf{Y'})/k_B T}} \quad (2.34)$$

We can define a "reduced" or marginal probability distribution as

$$p(x) = \int d\mathbf{Y'}\ P(x,\mathbf{Y'}) \quad (2.35)$$

which means

$$p(x) = \frac{\int d\mathbf{Y'}\ e^{-U(x,\mathbf{Y'})/k_B T}}{\int dx' \int d\mathbf{Y'}\ e^{-U(x',\mathbf{Y'})/k_B T}} \quad (2.36)$$

where the denominator is a normalization constant C. Note that the marginal distribution $p(x)$ may also be represented as the average of a delta function, $\langle \delta(x - x') \rangle$. Assuming that $p(x)$ can be expressed as a Boltzmann factor with some effective potential energy, let us define the quantity $W(x)$ as

$$W(x) \equiv -k_B T \ln[p(x)/C] \quad (2.37)$$

where C is a constant. To clarify the significance of $W(x)$, let us consider its derivative with respect to x,

$$
\begin{aligned}
\frac{\partial W}{\partial x} &= -k_{\mathrm{B}} T \frac{1}{p(x)} \frac{\partial p}{\partial x} \\
&= -k_{\mathrm{B}} T \frac{1}{\int d\mathbf{Y}' \, e^{-U(x,\mathbf{Y}')/k_{\mathrm{B}} T}} \int d\mathbf{Y}' \left(-\frac{1}{k_{\mathrm{B}} T} \frac{\partial U}{\partial x} \right) e^{-U(x,\mathbf{Y}')/k_{\mathrm{B}} T} \\
&= \frac{\int d\mathbf{Y}' \, (\partial U/\partial x) \, e^{-U(x,\mathbf{Y}')/k_{\mathrm{B}} T}}{\int d\mathbf{Y}' \, e^{-U(x,\mathbf{Y}')/k_{\mathrm{B}} T}} \\
&= \left\langle \frac{\partial U}{\partial x} \right\rangle_{(x)}
\end{aligned}
\tag{2.38}
$$

where the bracket means a conditional average over the $\mathbf{Y}$ degrees of freedom at a fixed value of x. By definition, the quantity $-\partial U/\partial x$ is the microscopic force, F_x, acting along the coordinate x. The expression above shows that the quantity $-\partial W/\partial x$ is equal to the average, or mean, force along the coordinate x. For this reason, $W(x)$ is called the "potential of mean force" or PMF [Kirkwood (1935)], as can be demonstrated by considering the reversible work,

$$
W(x) = W(x_0) - \int_{x_0}^{x} \langle F_x \rangle_{(x)} \, dx
\tag{2.39}
$$

Thus, the reversible work done along x is related to the marginal distribution $p(x)$. This profound relationship between an average mechanical quantity, $\langle \partial U/\partial x \rangle_{(x)}$, and a reduced statistical probability distribution, $p(x)$, is called the "reversible work theorem."

The PMF is a key concept in modern statistical mechanical theories of complex molecular systems. In particular, we will see in Chapter 9 that the transition rate between stable states can be expressed conveniently in terms of the function $W(x)$. Furthermore, for any observable $A(x)$ that depends only on the variable x,

$$
\begin{aligned}
\langle A \rangle &= \frac{\int dx \int d\mathbf{Y}' \, A(x) \, e^{-U/k_{\mathrm{B}} T}}{\int dx \int d\mathbf{Y}' \, e^{-U/k_{\mathrm{B}} T}} \\
&= \frac{\int dx \, A(x) \, e^{-W(x)/k_{\mathrm{B}} T}}{\int dx \, e^{-W(x)/k_{\mathrm{B}} T}}
\end{aligned}
\tag{2.40}
$$

The final expression for $\langle A \rangle$ is written as if the other degrees of freedom $\mathbf{Y}$ do not have to be written explicitly. In fact, their influence is taken into account implicitly via the effective potential $W(x)$. However, one has to be careful because $W(x)$ is actually temperature dependent. So, thermodynamic relations obtained via temperature derivative will need to incorporate terms like $\partial W/\partial T$.

It is often impractical to compute the marginal distribution directly from a computer simulation. For example, the presence of large energy barriers along x may prevent accurate sampling of the configurational space within the available computing times. To avoid such difficulties, special sampling techniques were designed to calculate the PMF effectively from the molecular trajectory. Eq. (2.39) offers a very practical strategy to compute the PMF along some interesting degrees of freedom from computer simulations. All one has to do is propagate the simulation with the coordinate x fixed, and then calculate the mean force $\langle F_x \rangle_{(x)}$. This procedure is then repeated for different values of x spanning the region of interest. The PMF is then directly determined by direct integration of the mean force according to Eq. (2.39), for example, using the trapezoidal rule,

$$W(x_n) = W(x_0) - \sum_{i=1}^{n-1} \frac{1}{2}\left[\langle F_x \rangle_{(x_i)} + \langle F_x \rangle_{(x_{i+1})} \right](x_{i+1} - x_i) \qquad (2.41)$$

Here we have assumed that x was a Cartesian coordinate (the situation with curvilinear variables is a little more complicated). An alternative method called "umbrella sampling" consists of collecting partial histograms of x obtained from simulations with different biasing potentials and then combining them together to generate an unbiased PMF [Torrie and Valleau (1974)].

The reversible work theorem can be extended to many dimensions, such that one can define the PMF for a single particle in three dimensions, $W(\mathbf{r})$, for example. More interestingly, one could also imagine integrating out all the solvent degrees of freedom to yield the PMF, $W(\mathbf{r}_1, \ldots, \mathbf{r}_n)$, for a dissolved molecular solute of n atoms,

$$\mathrm{e}^{-W(\mathbf{r}_1,\ldots,\mathbf{r}_n)/k_{\mathrm{B}}T} = C \int d\mathbf{Y}\, \mathrm{e}^{-U(\mathbf{r}_1,\ldots,\mathbf{r}_n;\mathbf{Y})/k_{\mathrm{B}}T} \qquad (2.42)$$

where $\mathbf{Y}$ represents the solvent coordinates and C is a constant. This concept is illustrated schematically in Figure 2.2. Such a PMF is an effective configuration-dependent free energy potential $W(\mathbf{r}_1, \ldots, \mathbf{r}_n)$ making no explicit reference to the solvent degrees of freedom. Incorporating the

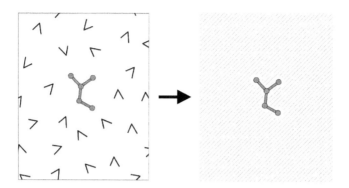

Fig. 2.2   Schematic representation of an atomic model of a molecular solute of n atoms surrounded by explicit water molecules (left) and of the same biomolecular solute in a solvent environment, which is taken into account implicitly.

influence of the solvent implicitly provides averages about the solute properties that are rigorously correct. All solvent effects are included implicitly in this PMF, such that no information about the influence of solvent on equilibrium properties is lost. Implicit solvent representations can be very useful conceptual tools for analyzing the results of simulations generated with explicit solvent molecules and to better understand the nature of solvation phenomena in general [Roux and Simonson (1999)].

Chapter 3

Solvation free energy

Computer simulations in which a large number of solvent molecules are treated explicitly represent one of the most detailed approaches to study complex biomolecules. Nevertheless, a significant computational cost is associated with the large number of solvent molecules required to model a bulk solution. In practice, a large fraction of computer time is spent calculating the trajectory of the solvent molecules, even though it is primarily the behavior of the solutes that is of interest. For this reason, it is desirable to develop a language and a set of conceptual tools to describe the influence of solvent on biomolecules. One of these conceptual tools is the solvation free energy, which plays an important role in understanding simulations generated with explicit solvent molecules.

3.1 Partition of solutes between two liquid phases

Let us consider n monoatomic solutes that are partitioning between two liquid phases. The situation is illustrated in Figure 3.1. The average number of solute particles on side 1 can be expressed as,

$$\langle n_1 \rangle = \frac{\int d\mathbf{X}\, n_1(\mathbf{X})\, e^{-U(\mathbf{X})/k_B T}}{\int d\mathbf{X}\, e^{-U(\mathbf{X})/k_B T}} \tag{3.1}$$

where the quantity $n_1(\mathbf{X})$ represents the instantaneous number of solute particles on side 1 for the configuration $\mathbf{X}$ of the system. A similar expression can be written for the average number of solute particles on side 2. The local solute concentration on side 1, C_1, is equal to $\langle n_1 \rangle / V_1$ and the local solute concentration on side 2, C_2, is equal to $\langle n_2 \rangle / V_2$, where V_1 and V_2 are the volumes of side 1 and 2, respectively.

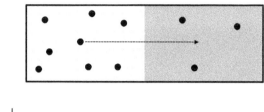

Fig. 3.1 Monoatomic solutes are partitioning between two liquid phases under equilibrium conditions (top). The solute partition is governed by the potential mean force (PMF), $W(\mathbf{r})$, of a tagged solute in the system (n.b., the PMF is represented pictorially in one dimension, but the point $\mathbf{r}$ is defined in three dimension throughout the entire system).

To proceed further, it is useful to introduce the step-function population operator, $H_1(\mathbf{r}_i)$, which is equal to 1 when a solute i is on side 1, and zero otherwise. A similar population operator $H_2(\mathbf{r}_i)$ can be defined for side 2. The average number of solute particles located on side 1 is then,

$$\langle n_1 \rangle = \left\langle \sum_i H_1(\mathbf{r}_i) \right\rangle$$

$$= \langle H_1(\mathbf{r}_1) \rangle + \langle H_1(\mathbf{r}_2) \rangle + \cdots \qquad (3.2)$$

Because all the different terms are equivalent, it is possible to express $\langle n_1 \rangle$ as an average with respect to a single solute particle,

$$\langle n_1 \rangle = n \langle H_1(\mathbf{r}_1) \rangle \qquad (3.3)$$

Essentially, all the solute molecules are identical, so we can focus our attention on any one of them (from here, we will drop the label of the solute particle for simplicity). Therefore,

$$\langle n_1 \rangle = \frac{\int d\mathbf{r}\, H_1(\mathbf{r}) \int d\mathbf{Y}\, e^{-U(\mathbf{r},\mathbf{Y})/k_B T}}{\int d\mathbf{r} \int d\mathbf{Y}\, e^{-U(\mathbf{r},\mathbf{Y})/k_B T}}$$

$$= \frac{\int d\mathbf{r}\, H_1(\mathbf{r})\, e^{-W(\mathbf{r})/k_B T}}{\int d\mathbf{r}\, e^{-W(\mathbf{r})/k_B T}} \qquad (3.4)$$

where $\mathbf{r}$ is the coordinate of a tagged solute particle, and $\mathbf{Y}$ represents the coordinates of all the remaining atoms of the two liquid phases (including solvent and all the other solute particles). A similar expression will be for $\langle n_2 \rangle$, the average number of solute particles located on side 2.

Here, $W(\mathbf{r})$ is the PMF for a single tagged solute within the system (all other degrees of freedom have been integrated out). Given these expressions for the average numbers of solute particles on sides 1 and 2, the local concentrations on sides 1 and 2 are equal to $C_1 = n\langle H_1 \rangle / V_1$ and $C_2 = n\langle H_2 \rangle / V_2$, respectively. As illustrated in Figure 3.1, the PMF of a tagged solute particle is expected to be essentially equal to a constant in each of the uniform liquid phases, with some possible abrupt changes over a microscopic length scale at the liquid–liquid interface. This implies that the ratio of the average population operator is

$$\frac{\langle H_1 \rangle}{\langle H_2 \rangle} = \frac{\int d\mathbf{r}\; H_1(\mathbf{r})\; e^{-W(\mathbf{r})/k_B T}}{\int d\mathbf{r}\; H_2(\mathbf{r})\; e^{-W(\mathbf{r})/k_B T}}$$

$$\approx \frac{e^{-W_1/k_B T} \times \int d\mathbf{r}\; H_1(\mathbf{r})}{e^{-W_2/k_B T} \times \int d\mathbf{r}\; H_2(\mathbf{r})}$$

$$\approx \frac{e^{-W_1/k_B T} \times V_1}{e^{-W_2/k_B T} \times V_2} \tag{3.5}$$

where V_1 and V_2 are the volumes of sides 1 and 2, respectively. It is assumed that the contribution from the microscopic interfacial region to the volume integral is negligible. Accordingly, it can be shown that

$$\Delta W = W_1 - W_2 = -k_B T \ln\left(\frac{C_1}{C_2}\right) \tag{3.6}$$

Equation (3.6) provides a fundamental relation between the relative free energy of a solute in equilibrium partition between two liquid phases and the concentration of this solute in these two liquid phases. This relation allows one to determine ΔW experimentally by measuring the concentrations. If $C_1 > C_2$, then $\Delta W < 0$, as is illustrated in Figure 3.1.

It is important to note that, while the above expression was derived for a monoatomic solute, it is also valid for a molecular solute simply by considering that $\mathbf{r}$ corresponds to some reference position (such as the center of mass) associated with the solute.

The quantity ΔW becomes the absolute solvation free energy of the solute when side 2 is vacuum, $\Delta W = W_{\text{solvent}} - W_{\text{vacuum}}$. This is a particularly important quantity, especially in the development and validation of force fields designed to match experimental data. The absolute solvation free energy of a solute may be expressed as,

$$e^{-\Delta W/k_B T} = \frac{\int d\mathbf{Y} \; e^{-U(\mathbf{r},\mathbf{Y})/k_B T} \Big|_{\mathbf{r} \in \text{ solvent}}}{\int d\mathbf{Y} \; e^{-U(\mathbf{r},\mathbf{Y})/k_B T} \Big|_{\mathbf{r} \in \text{ vacuum}}} \tag{3.7}$$

Because the liquid phase and the vacuum region of the system are uniform, the solute can be fixed at any position $\mathbf{r}^{\text{vac}}$ and $\mathbf{r}^{\text{liq}}$ to define the absolute free energy.

The absolute free energy may be expressed in a visual fashion as,

$$e^{-\Delta W/k_B T} = \underline{\qquad\qquad\qquad\qquad} \tag{3.8}$$

with $\int d\mathbf{Y}$ (solute in solvent, $\leftarrow$ solute in solvent) over $\int d\mathbf{Y}$ (solute in vacuum, $\leftarrow$ solute in vacuum)

Here, the solute is fixed in both the numerator and denominator (we implicitly assume that the solvent molecules are confined to remain at the bottom of the container in the configurational integrals). The numerator is a Boltzmann configurational integral with normal potential energy with all interactions, while the denominator is a Boltzmann configurational integral in which the solute is decoupled from the solvent (all solute–solvent interactions are zero because the solute is too far away from the solvent). If we define the artificial potential energy function U^* in which the solute is "invisible" to the solvent (decoupled), we can express the absolute solvation free energy as

$$e^{-\Delta W/k_B T} = \frac{\int d\mathbf{Y} \; e^{-U(\mathbf{r},\mathbf{Y})/k_B T}}{\int d\mathbf{Y} \; e^{-U^*(\mathbf{r},\mathbf{Y})/k_B T}} \tag{3.9}$$

or in a more visual fashion as,

$$e^{-\Delta W/k_B T} = \frac{\int d\mathbf{Y} \quad \boxed{\quad \bullet \quad} \quad \leftarrow \text{interacting solute } U}{\int d\mathbf{Y} \quad \boxed{\quad \circ \quad} \quad \leftarrow \text{decoupled solute } U^*} \tag{3.10}$$

3.2 Thermodynamic integration

The above discussion leading to Eq. (3.10) opens the way to define a powerful route to compute the solvation free energy of a solute. Let us construct the artificial energy

$$U(\lambda) = (1 - \lambda)U^* + \lambda U \tag{3.11}$$

where λ is a thermodynamic coupling parameter. The potential energy is normal and the solute interacts with the solvent molecules when $\lambda = 1$, whereas the potential energy is U^* and the solute is decoupled when $\lambda = 0$. Then we can define the λ-dependent solvation free energy

$$e^{-\Delta W(\lambda)/k_B T} = \frac{\int d\mathbf{Y} \ e^{-U(\mathbf{r}, \mathbf{Y}; \lambda)/k_B T}}{\int d\mathbf{Y} \ e^{-U(\mathbf{r}, \mathbf{Y}; \lambda=0)/k_B T}} \tag{3.12}$$

Let us consider $\partial \Delta W(\lambda)/\partial \lambda$. It is easy to show that

$$\frac{\partial \Delta W}{\partial \lambda} = \left\langle \frac{\partial U}{\partial \lambda} \right\rangle_{(\lambda)} \tag{3.13}$$

where the bracket represent an average

$$\langle \ldots \rangle_{(\lambda)} = \frac{\int d\mathbf{Y} \cdots e^{-U(\lambda)/k_B T}}{\int d\mathbf{Y} \ e^{-U(\lambda)/k_B T}} \tag{3.14}$$

It follows that

$$\Delta W(1) = \Delta W(0) + \int_0^1 d\lambda \left\langle \frac{\partial U}{\partial \lambda} \right\rangle_{(\lambda)} \tag{3.15}$$

This procedure is referred to as thermodynamic integration (TI) [Kirkwood (1935)]. The above development is very similar to the expressions for the mean force that we encountered previously in Chapter 2. Note the analogy with Eq. (2.37) relating the derivative of the potential mean force (PMF) with the average of the microscopic force. With respect to the solvation free energy, the quantity $\partial U/\partial \lambda$ is like a generalized thermodynamic force. We have essentially complete freedom in the manner we choose to introduce λ, as long as the two end states U^* and U are recovered. For example, in certain cases, it will be advantageous to use the charge of the solute as the thermodynamic coupling parameter (see below). By convention, $\Delta W(0)$ is typically set to zero if the reference side is a vacuum (though there are sometimes different conventions used in different contexts).

To utilize the TI formulation in practice, one must carry out a number of separate simulations for different values of λ between 0 and 1, compute the average $\langle \partial U/\partial \lambda \rangle_{(\lambda)}$, and then perform the numerical integral of Eq. (3.15). The alternative route consists of breaking down the total free energy into finite increments

$$\Delta W(1) = [\Delta W(1) - \Delta W(0.9)] + [\Delta W(0.9) - \Delta W(0.8)] + \cdots$$
$$\cdots + [\Delta W(0.1) - \Delta W(0)] \qquad (3.16)$$

where the free energy difference $[\Delta W(\lambda_{i+1}) - \Delta W(\lambda_i)]$ can be expressed as [Zwanzig (1954)],

$$e^{-[\Delta W(\lambda_{i+1}) - \Delta W(\lambda_i)]/k_B T} = \frac{\int d\mathbf{Y} \; e^{-U(\lambda_{i+1})/k_B T}}{\int d\mathbf{Y} \; e^{-U(\lambda_i)/k_B T}}$$

$$= \frac{\int d\mathbf{Y} \; e^{-[U(\lambda_{i+1}) - U(\lambda_i)]/k_B T} \; e^{-U(\lambda_i)/k_B T}}{\int d\mathbf{Y} \; e^{-U(\lambda_i)/k_B T}}$$

$$= \left\langle e^{-[U(\lambda_{i+1}) - U(\lambda_i)]/k_B T} \right\rangle_{(\lambda_i)} \qquad (3.17)$$

(where we implicitly assumed that $\Delta W(0) = 0$). This procedure is referred to as free energy perturbation (FEP) [McCammon and Straatsma (1992); Kollman (1993)]. To utilize the FEP formulation, one must carry out a number of separate simulations for different values of λ between 0 and 1, compute the averages in Eq. (3.17), and then add all the free energy increments together.

3.3   Decomposition of the free energy

One could express the total solvation free energy of a monoatomic ion of charge Q in water, by relying on the potential energy U for the normal ion solute with all interactions, and the artificial potential energy U^* for the noninteracting decoupled ion solute. One could also proceed by stages, by introducing an intermediate state with the potential energy U^{**} corresponding to the uncharged solute (its charge turned off). Mutiplying this equation

$$e^{-\Delta W/k_{\mathrm{B}}T} = \frac{\int d\mathbf{Y} \; e^{-U/k_{\mathrm{B}}T}}{\int d\mathbf{Y} \; e^{-U^*/k_{\mathrm{B}}T}} \tag{3.18}$$

by 1, written as,

$$1 = \frac{\int d\mathbf{Y} \; e^{-U^{**}/k_{\mathrm{B}}T}}{\int d\mathbf{Y} \; e^{-U^{**}/k_{\mathrm{B}}T}} \tag{3.19}$$

yields,

$$e^{-\Delta W/k_{\mathrm{B}}T} = \frac{\int d\mathbf{Y} \; e^{-U^{**}/k_{\mathrm{B}}T}}{\int d\mathbf{Y} \; e^{-U^*/k_{\mathrm{B}}T}} \times \frac{\int d\mathbf{Y} \; e^{-U/k_{\mathrm{B}}T}}{\int d\mathbf{Y} \; e^{-U^{**}/k_{\mathrm{B}}T}} \tag{3.20}$$

The simple procedure to introduce any chosen intermediate states U^{**} can be used to express the total free energy in terms of well-defined contributions [Roux and Simonson (1999)]. This can be very useful because intermolecular forces are dominated by harsh repulsive short-range interactions, arising from Pauli's exclusion principle, van der Waals attractive forces arising from quantum dispersion, and long-range electrostatic interactions, arising from the nonuniform charge distribution. It is convenient to express the interaction energy of the monoatomic solute with the solvent as a sum of electrostatic contributions and the remaining "core" nonpolar contributions. This simple procedure yields,

$$e^{-\Delta W/k_{\mathrm{B}}T} = \frac{\int d\mathbf{Y} \; e^{-U(\text{core \& no charge})/k_{\mathrm{B}}T}}{\int d\mathbf{Y} \; e^{-U(\text{no core \& no charge})/k_{\mathrm{B}}T}}$$

$$\times \frac{\int d\mathbf{Y} \; e^{-U(\text{core \& charge})/k_{\mathrm{B}}T}}{\int d\mathbf{Y} \; e^{-U(\text{core \& no charge})/k_{\mathrm{B}}T}}$$

$$= e^{-\Delta W_{\mathrm{np}}/k_{\mathrm{B}}T} \times e^{-\Delta W_{\mathrm{elec}}/k_{\mathrm{B}}T} \tag{3.21}$$

with

$$\Delta W = \Delta W_{\mathrm{np}} + \Delta W_{\mathrm{elec}} \tag{3.22}$$

Here, the first term corresponds to the solvation free energy of an equivalent but uncharged solute, while the second term corresponds to the so-called "charging free energy" of the monoatomic ion in the solvent. Accordingly, the total free energy of the solute may be expressed rigorously as the reversible thermodynamic work needed to construct the system in a step-by-step process. At the first step, the nonpolar solute–solvent interactions are switched "on" in the absence of any solute–solvent electrostatic interactions; in the second step, the solute–solvent electrostatic interactions are switched "on" in the presence of the solute–solvent nonpolar interactions.

3.4   Solvation of nonpolar molecules

To clarify the significance of ΔW_{np}, let us first consider the special case of a nonpolar molecule dissolved in liquid water. Modern understanding of the hydrophobic effect attributes it primarily to weakening of hydrogen bonds between water molecules when they are near a nonpolar surface. This view is confirmed by computer simulations of nonpolar solutes in water. To a first approximation, the magnitude of the free energy associated with the nonpolar contribution can be considered to be proportional to the number of solvent molecules in the first solvation shell. The idea is based on the assumption that the nonpolar free energy contribution is directly related to the solvent-accessible surface area (SASA) [Lee and Richards (1971)],

$$\Delta W_{\mathrm{np}} = \gamma \mathcal{S}_{\mathrm{tot}} \qquad (3.23)$$

where γ has the dimension of surface tension and $\mathcal{S}_{\mathrm{tot}}$ is the SASA of the solute. The SASA is normally determined by "rolling" a solvent molecule all over the surface of each solute (Figure 3.2). This leads to a convenient and attractive approximation that is widely used in biophysical applications [Sharp *et al.* (1991a,b)]. It is expected that there should be a close relationship between γ, the macroscopic oil–water surface tension, interfacial free energies, and the magnitude of the hydrophobic effect [Tanford (1979)]. The value of γ is typically around 20 to $30\,\mathrm{cal/mol/Å^2}$, while the macroscopic oil–water surface tension is around 70 $\mathrm{cal/mol/Å^2}$ [Tanford (1979)]. The difference between the optimal parameter γ for alkanes and the true macroscopic surface tension for oil–water interfaces reflects the influence of the microscopic length scale and the crudeness of the SASA model. A simple statistical mechanics approach describing the free energy of inserting hard spheres in water called scaled particle theory (SPT) provides an important conceptual basis for understanding some of the limitations of SASA models [Stillinger (1973)].

The consequences of this simple approximation to the nonpolar free energy contribution based on Eq. (3.23) points to two facets of the hydrophobic effect. The positive (unfavorable) free energy ΔW of a nonpolar solute in water is often referred to as the "hydrophobic solvation." The changes in the SASA upon the association of two nonpolar solutes is illustrated in Figure 3.2. When the two solutes come into direct contact,

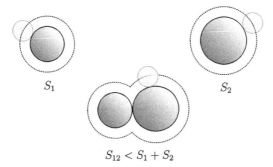

$$S_{12} < S_1 + S_2$$

Fig. 3.2 Changes in the solvent-accessible surface area (SASA) $\mathcal{S}$ caused by the association of two nonpolar solutes in solvent. The SASA (dash lines) is determined by "rolling" a solvent molecule all over the surface of each solute.

the total SASA, $\mathcal{S}_{\text{tot}} = \mathcal{S}_{12}$, is smaller than the total SASA, $\mathcal{S}_{\text{tot}} = \mathcal{S}_1 + \mathcal{S}_2$, when they are well separated from one another. This gives rise to a favorable interaction between the two nonpolar solutes. This interaction between two nonpolar solutes is often referred to as the "hydrophobic interaction." While these results are intuitively reasonable and appealing in their clarity, it is important to keep in mind that Eq. (3.23) is an extremely oversimplified representation of the nonpolar contribution to the solvation free energy.

3.5 Electrostatics and Born model of ion solvation

To clarify the significance of ΔW_{elec}, let us first consider the charging of a spherical ion in water. If we choose the charge of the ion as the coupling parameter, electrostatic free energy contribution in Eq. (3.22) may be expressed as a thermodynamic integration corresponding to a reversible charging process.

$$\Delta W_{\text{elec}} = \int_0^{Q_{\text{ion}}} dQ' \left\langle \frac{\partial U}{\partial Q'} \right\rangle_{(Q')} \qquad (3.24)$$

Starting from the expression for the charging free energy, Eq. (3.24), we write

$$\frac{\partial U}{\partial Q} = \frac{\partial}{\partial Q} \left(\sum_i \frac{Q q_i}{|\mathbf{r}_{\text{ion}} - \mathbf{r}_i|} + \text{"other terms independent of } Q\text{"} \right)$$

$$= \sum_i \frac{q_i}{|\mathbf{r}_{\text{ion}} - \mathbf{r}_i|}$$

$$= \Phi(\mathbf{r}_{\text{ion}}) \qquad (3.25)$$

where $\Phi(\mathbf{r})$ is the electrostatic potential arising from the solvent felt by the ion at position $\mathbf{r}_{\mathrm{ion}}$. The thermodynamic integration can then be written as,

$$\Delta W_{\mathrm{elec}} \equiv \int_0^{Q_{\mathrm{ion}}} dQ' \ \langle \Phi \rangle_{(Q')} \tag{3.26}$$

where $\langle \Phi \rangle_{(Q')}$ is the "reaction field," that is, the average electrostatic potential exerted on the ion by the solvent that it has polarized,

$$\langle \Phi \rangle_{(Q')} = \int d\mathbf{r} \ \frac{1}{r} \ \langle \rho_{\mathrm{elec}}(\mathbf{r}) \rangle_{(Q')} \tag{3.27}$$

(for the sake of simplicity, it is assumed that the ion is fixed at the origin and that $\mathbf{r}_{\mathrm{ion}} = 0$). As illustrated in Figure 3.3, simple approximation regarding the structure of the solvent around an ion lead to the Born model of solvation. Because the solvent charge density, $\langle \rho_{\mathrm{elec}}(\mathbf{r}) \rangle_{(Q')}$, is a sharply peaked function near the radius of the ion, one can write,

$$\Delta W_{\mathrm{elec}} = \int_0^{Q_{\mathrm{ion}}} dQ' \int d\mathbf{r} \ \frac{1}{r} \ \langle \rho_{\mathrm{elec}}(\mathbf{r}) \rangle_{(Q')}$$

$$\approx \frac{1}{R_{\mathrm{ion}}} \int_0^{Q_{\mathrm{ion}}} dQ' \underbrace{\int d\mathbf{r} \ \langle \rho_{\mathrm{elec}}(\mathbf{r}) \rangle_{(Q')}}_{\text{total solvent charge } Q_{\mathrm{solvent}}} \tag{3.28}$$

The total charge Q_{solvent} induced within the solvent in reaction to the presence of the ion is a function of Q'. Simple considerations can establish its value. According to Gauss's Law, the total electric field at a large distance from the ion is,

$$\frac{1}{4\pi} \int \mathbf{E} \cdot d\mathbf{a} = Q_{\mathrm{tot}} \tag{3.29}$$

enclosed by the Gaussian surface, where $\mathbf{E} = Q_{\mathrm{tot}}/r^2$. The total charge enclosed by the surface is the charge of the ion (Q') and the charge induced by polarization of the solvent, $Q_{\mathrm{tot}} = Q' + Q_{\mathrm{solvent}}$. Macroscopically, we also know that the average electric field at a large distance from the ion of

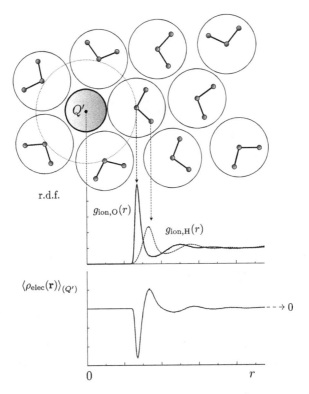

Fig. 3.3 Molecular basis of the Born model of ion solvation [Roux *et al.* (1990)]. An ion of positive charge Q' (grey) is surrounded by water molecules (top). The thin dotted circle roughly indicates the distance of the water oxygen from the first hydration shell around the ion (top). The ion-oxygen and ion-hydrogen radial distribution functions (r.d.f.), $g_{\mathrm{ion,O}}(r)$ and $g_{\mathrm{ion,H}}(r)$, display first main peaks corresponding to the first hydration shell. Assuming that the charge Q' is positive, the solvent charge density shown at the bottom, $\langle \rho_{\mathrm{elec}}(\mathbf{r}) \rangle_{(Q')}$, displays a negative peak (arising from the negative water oxygen) followed by a smaller positive peak (arising from the positive water hydrogen). As the distance r becomes large, the solvent charge density decays to zero.

charge Q' should be $\mathbf{E} = Q'/(\epsilon_{\mathrm{w}} r^2)$. Thus, $Q_{\mathrm{tot}} = Q'/\epsilon_{\mathrm{w}}$ and

$$Q_{\mathrm{solvent}} = \frac{Q'}{\epsilon_{\mathrm{w}}} - Q'$$

$$= Q'\left(\frac{1}{\epsilon_{\mathrm{w}}} - 1\right) \tag{3.30}$$

Hence, the charging free energy of the ion is [Roux *et al.* (1990)],

$$
\Delta W_{\text{elec}} = \frac{1}{R_{\text{ion}}} \int_0^{Q_{\text{ion}}} dQ' \, Q' \left(\frac{1}{\epsilon_{\text{w}}} - 1 \right)
$$

$$
= \frac{1}{2} \frac{Q_{\text{ion}}^2}{R_{\text{ion}}} \left(\frac{1}{\epsilon_{\text{w}}} - 1 \right) \tag{3.31}
$$

This model of ion solvation was first derived by Born in 1920 using continuum electrostatic arguments [Born (1920)].

In the continuum approximation, the reaction field from the solvent is linearly related to the charge of the solute,

$$
\langle \Phi \rangle_{(Q_{\text{ion}})} = \frac{Q_{\text{ion}}}{R_{\text{ion}}} \left(\frac{1}{\epsilon_{\text{w}}} - 1 \right) \tag{3.32}
$$

The charging free energy should be clearly distinguished from the average electrostatic interaction energy between the ion and the solvent, $\langle U_{\text{ion}-\text{solvent}} \rangle = Q_{\text{ion}} \langle \Phi \rangle_{(Q_{\text{ion}})}$. Comparison of these expressions shows $\Delta W_{\text{elec}} = \frac{1}{2} \langle U_{\text{ion}-\text{solvent}} \rangle$. The factor of one-half is a characteristic signature of the linear electrostatic response of the solvent, which is often observed in calculations based on simulations with explicit solvent. These arguments may be extended to represent the charging free energy of a molecular solute using continuum electrostatics.

Chapter 4

Implicit solvent and continuum models

We have seen that the charging free energy of a simple monoatomic solute can be approximated by representing the surrounding solvent as a dielectric continuum. It can be shown that this type of treatment leads to the Born model [Born (1920)], which was established long ago. More generally, continuum electrostatics approximations in which the solvent is represented as a featureless dielectric medium are very popular approaches to represent the influence of solvent on biological molecules. An additional factor that greatly affects the solvation forces acting on biomolecules is the influence of salt in the solution.

4.1 The Poisson–Boltzmann equation

To proceed beyond the simple case of a monoatomic ion, let us consider a molecular solute of arbitrary shape in a dielectric medium (Figure 4.1). Let us assume that the molecular solute comprises several atomic charges q_i. In principle, the charging free energy of the molecular solute can be derived from the reaction field of the solvent at the position of these atomic charges,

$$\Delta W_{\text{elec}} = \sum_i \frac{1}{2} q_i \Phi_{\text{rf}}(i) \qquad (4.1)$$

where $\langle \phi_{\text{rf}}(i) \rangle$ is the solvent reaction field at the position of atom i. The factor of one-half appears in Eq. (4.1) as a result of the linear dielectric response of the solvent. The solvent reaction field is calculated by solving

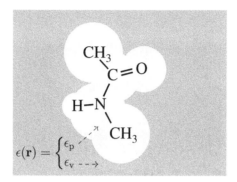

Fig. 4.1   Molecular solute of arbitrary shape in a dielectric medium.

the Poisson equation for macroscopic media:

$$\nabla \cdot [\epsilon(\mathbf{r})\nabla\phi] = -4\pi\rho(\mathbf{r}) \tag{4.2}$$

where $\epsilon(\mathbf{r})$ is the position-dependent dielectric constant, $\phi(\mathbf{r})$ is the electrostatic potential, and $\rho(\mathbf{r})$ is the charge distribution of the solute at position $\mathbf{r}$ (excluding charges from the dielectric material). The charge density from the solute is a sum over all atomic charges,

$$\rho(\mathbf{r}) = \sum_i q_i\delta(\mathbf{r} - \mathbf{r}_i) \tag{4.3}$$

and the dielectric constant at a point, $\mathbf{r}$, is defined as a function of the position of all the atoms of the solute,

$$\epsilon(\mathbf{r}) = 1 + (\epsilon_s - 1)H(\mathbf{r}) \tag{4.4}$$

where ϵ_s is the dielectric constant of the solvent and $H(\mathbf{r})$ is a volume exclusion indicator step-function that is equal to 1 in the solvent region and zero in the interior of the solute [Roux *et al.* (1990); Nina *et al.* (1997)]. There are several conventions to construct the volume exclusion function $H(\mathbf{r})$ and define the space-dependent function $\epsilon(\mathbf{r})$. In a simple case, $H(\mathbf{r})$ may be defined in terms of overlapping atomic spherical exclusion functions:

$$H(\mathbf{r}) = \prod_i H_i(|\mathbf{r} - \mathbf{r}_i|) \tag{4.5}$$

where k_B is Boltzmann's constant, T is the absolute temperature, and $H_i(|\mathbf{r} - \mathbf{r}_i|)$ is a radially symmetric atomic volume exclusion function that describes the distribution of solvent particles around atom i. Furthermore, as illustrated in the microscopic derivation of the Born model, the dielectric boundary is closely related to the nearest density peak in the solute–solvent distribution function. The atomic radii that are optimal for setting the protein–water dielectric interface may differ from the optimal atomic radii needed to set the ion-accessible region near the protein surface.

To determine the solvent reaction field, the Poisson equation must be solved twice: once with the uniform dielectric constant equal to 1, to obtain the potential for a reference vacuum state (ϕ_v), and once with the nonuniform dielectric constant $\epsilon(\mathbf{r})$, to obtain the potential for the solvated state (ϕ_s). The reaction field is then $\Phi_{rf} = [\phi_s - \phi_v]$. The effect of electrolytes in the solvent can be included in the Poisson equation by assuming that the ion density throughout the solvent depends only on the local total electrostatic potential in a mean-field manner,

$$\langle \rho_{\text{ions}}(\mathbf{r}) \rangle = H(\mathbf{r}) \sum_\alpha q_\alpha [C_\alpha] e^{-q_\alpha \phi(\mathbf{r})/k_B T} \tag{4.6}$$

where $H(\mathbf{r})$ is the volume exclusion function, α refers to a specific type of mobile ion, and $[C_\alpha]$ is its overall concentration. In principle, the regions accessible to the high dielectric water and mobile ions do not have to coincide; they could be different. Inserting this charge density into the Poisson equation for macroscopic media yields the nonlinear form of the Poisson–Boltzmann (PB) equation,

$$\nabla \cdot [\epsilon(\mathbf{r}) \nabla \phi(\mathbf{r})] = -4\pi \left(\rho(\mathbf{r}) + H(\mathbf{r}) \sum_\alpha q_\alpha [C_\alpha] e^{-q_\alpha \phi(\mathbf{r})/k_B T} \right) \tag{4.7}$$

Linearization of Eq. (4.7) with respect to the potential ϕ yields the familiar Debye–Hückel approximation or linearized PB equation [Debye and Hückel (1923); Fowler and Guggenheim (1939)]:

$$\nabla \cdot [\epsilon(\mathbf{r}) \nabla \phi(\mathbf{r})] - \bar{\kappa}^2(\mathbf{r}) \phi(\mathbf{r}) = -4\pi \rho(\mathbf{r}) \tag{4.8}$$

where $\bar{\kappa}^2(\mathbf{r})$ is the space-dependent screening factor, which varies from zero, in the solvent-excluded regions, to $4\pi \sum_\alpha q_\alpha^2 [C_\alpha]/k_B T$, in the bulk solvent. The PB equation (linear and nonlinear) is a particularly simple and powerful approach to address questions about the influence of salt on complex biological systems. In ionic solutions, all electrostatic potentials are screened by the factor κ,

$$\kappa^2 = \frac{4\pi}{k_B T \epsilon_w} \sum_\alpha q_\alpha^2 [C_\alpha] \tag{4.9}$$

over a length scale $\Lambda = 1/\kappa$ called the Debye length. For example, a 1:1 solution of electrolyte in water at 25°C and a concentration of 1 mM has a Debye length of 96 Å, corresponding to roughly 40 water diameters; whereas at a concentration of 100 mM the Debye length is 9.6 Å, equivalent to just four water diameters. At higher concentrations, when the Debye length becomes comparable to molecular dimensions, the Debye–Hückel theory is not expected to apply (steric exclusion effects and ion correlations come into play).

Added note: Solution of the PB equation for a planar charged wall

Let us consider a planar wall carrying a charge per unit area of σ and in contact with a 1:1 aqueous salt solution of concentration $[C]$. We assume that the entire system is symmetric along x and that the electric field E is nonzero only on the side of the electrolyte solution. We wish to determine the potential and the charge in the solution. The PB equation reduces to the one-dimensional differential equation:

$$\frac{d^2\phi(x)}{dx^2} - \kappa^2\phi(x) = 0 \tag{4.10}$$

which has two possible solutions:

$$\phi(x) = Ae^{\pm\kappa x} \tag{4.11}$$

where A is a constant. We retain only the physical case of the decaying exponential such that $\lim x \to \infty\ \phi(x) = 0$. Given the surface charge of σ, we have that the electric field at the surface of the wall must obey:

$$E = \frac{4\pi\sigma}{\epsilon_w}$$

$$= -\phi(x)\Big|_{x=0}$$

$$= A\kappa e^{-\kappa x}\Big|_0$$

$$= A\kappa \tag{4.12}$$

thus,

$$\phi(x) = \left(\frac{4\pi\sigma}{\kappa\epsilon_w}\right)e^{-\kappa x} \tag{4.13}$$

We can see that the electrostatic potential decays exponentially as a function of the distance from the wall, with a length scale $1/\kappa \equiv \Lambda$. This is the Debye length. The charge density in the salt solution for a 1:1 electrolyte is

$$\rho(x) = -\left(\frac{2q^2[C]}{k_B T}\right)\phi(x) \tag{4.14}$$

Integrating the total charge in the ionic solution per unit area yields:

$$
\int_0^\infty \rho(x)\,dx = -\left(\frac{2q^2[C]}{k_BT}\right)\int_0^\infty \left(\frac{4\pi\sigma}{\kappa\epsilon_w}\right)e^{-\kappa x}\,dx
$$

$$
= -\left(\frac{2q^2[C]}{k_BT}\right)\left(\frac{4\pi\sigma}{\kappa\epsilon_w}\right)\frac{e^{-\kappa x}}{-\kappa}\bigg|_0^\infty
$$

$$
= -\left(\frac{8\pi q^2[C]}{\epsilon_w k_BT}\right)\left(\frac{1}{\kappa^2}\right)\sigma
$$

$$
= -\sigma \tag{4.15}
$$

which exactly compensates for the charge of the wall (this is why $\lim x \to \infty\ \phi(x) = 0$).

4.2 Nernst membrane potential

An electrical potential difference can be established across a semi-permeable membrane separating two ionic solutions of different concentrations. The potential results from a balance between the entropic tendency to homogenize the system, and the necessity to maintain local charge neutrality as much as possible. The struggle between these two opposing forces takes place in the region of the semi-permeable membrane, and the potential difference is the result of this interfacial phenomena. In this situation, which corresponds to thermodynamic equilibrium, the bulk ionic solutions remain electrically neutral and the potential difference across the membrane arises from a very small imbalance of net charges on each side of the membrane. The origin of the membrane potential is illustrated with a simple example shown in Figure 4.2. The membrane potential difference follows from Eq. (3.6) by assuming that the PMF is dominated by the overall electrostatic potential, $W = q\phi$,

$$
\phi_1 - \phi_2 = -\frac{k_BT}{q}\ln\left(\frac{[C_1]}{[C_2]}\right) \tag{4.16}
$$

where q is the charge of the ion that is permeable through the semi-membrane and $[C_1]$ and $[C_2]$ are the salt concentrations on sides 1 and 2, respectively. The Nernst potential across the membrane is caused directly by a small imbalance of net charges on each side of the membrane. Despite the potential, the ionic solutions obey the electroneutrality condition macroscopically. The situation is very similar to that of a parallel plate capacitor made of a slab of insulator (the lipid membrane) with a good conductor on either side (the ionic solutions).

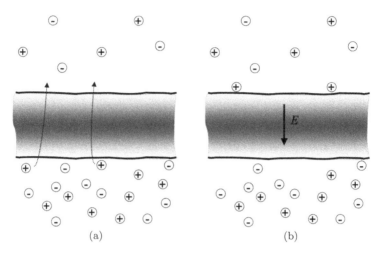

(a)   (b)

Fig. 4.2   We consider a semi-permeable membrane separating two compartments. The membrane is only permeable to the cations. The ion concentration in the bottom compartment is 10 times larger than the concentration in the upper compartment. In (a), the number of anions (−) and cations (+) is initially equal on both sides of the membrane (charge neutrality), but the number of ions is larger in the lower compartment than in the upper compartment. Because the membrane is semi-permeable to the cations, then, as there are 10 times more cations in the bottom compartment than in the top compartment, there will be 10 times more chances of a cation crossing up than down. This diffusive flow, which is proportional to the concentration gradient, increases the charge of the top compartment by one positive charge and the charge of the lower compartment by one negative charge, producing a charge separation. This charge separation introduces a new nonrandom electrostatic force acting on ions, which tends to drive cations from the top compartment back into the bottom compartment. This situation is schematically pictured in (b). The final result is that charge separation will build up a voltage difference across the membrane, and the equilibrium is reached when the electrostatic force balances the diffusive flow produced by the concentration gradient. When that happens, any ion that crosses in one direction will be counterbalanced, on average, by another one crossing in the opposite direction, maintaining an equilibrium situation.

Added note: Nernst potential

The concentration of K^+ inside the cell is about 160 mM, while it is about 10 mM outside the cell.

$$\Delta\phi = -\frac{1.38 \times 10^{-23}(\text{J/K})\,273.15(\text{K})}{1.602 \times 10^{-19}\text{Coul}} \ln\left(\frac{[160\text{mM}]}{[10\text{mM}]}\right) \tag{4.17}$$

$$= -23.53\text{mV} \times 2.77 \tag{4.18}$$

$$= -65\text{mV} \tag{4.19}$$

This yields a Nernst potential of −65 mV inside the cell relative to the outside. This value reflects the membrane potential under resting conditions, indicating that the basal state of the cell membrane is to be largely impermeable to all ions except K^+. On the other hand, the concentration of Na^+ inside the cell is about 10 mM, while it is about 150 mM outside the cell, which yields a potential of +63 mV inside the cell relative to outside. The situation where the membrane potential is dominated by the Na^+ concentration gradient corresponds to a depolarized state of the cell membrane.

In the presence of a membrane potential, the bulk solution remains electrically neutral and a small charge imbalance is distributed in the neighborhood of the interfaces. The charge imbalance is distributed in a layer of thickness κ^{-1} in the neighborhood of the interface, that is, within a distance of the order of the Debye length from the membrane ($\sim$9 Å). Since a physiological concentration of KCl (150 mM) represents approximately one K^+ cation and one Cl^- anion per volume of $(22\text{ Å})^3$, the Nernst potential is caused by a strikingly small accumulation of net charge relative to the average ion density. The capacitance of a typical lipid membrane is on the order of 1 μF/cm^2, which corresponds to a thickness of approximately 25 Å and a dielectric constant of 2 for the hydrophobic core of a bilayer. Typical physiological conditions correspond to a membrane potential on the order of 100 mV and a salt concentration of 150 mM. In this situation, the net charge per area is $CV_{mp} = 10^{-7}$Coul/cm^2, which corresponds to only one atomic unit charge per surface of $(130\text{ Å})^2$.

To go beyond these simple considerations, it is necessary to determine the spatial variation of the potential. Let the fraction of the electrostatic transmembrane potential be represented by the dimensionless function $\phi_{mp}(\mathbf{r}_i)$, which can be calculated by solving a modified version of the linear PB equation [Roux (1997)],

$$\nabla \cdot [\epsilon(\mathbf{r})\nabla\phi_{mp}(\mathbf{r})] - \bar{\kappa}^2(\mathbf{r})[\phi_{mp}(\mathbf{r}) - \Theta(\mathbf{r})] = 0 \qquad (4.20)$$

where the function $\Theta(\mathbf{r})$ is equal to 1 on the side of the membrane, which is in contact with the bulk solution set to the reference potential V, and zero otherwise. The Θ function in Eq. (4.20) insures that the mobile ions are in equilibrium with the bath with which they are in contact. $\phi_{mp}(\mathbf{r})$ is a dimensionless function equal to the fraction of the total membrane potential V_{mp}. In the case of a perfectly planar system, the electric field across the membrane is constant and ϕ_{mp} varies linearly in the membrane (for this reason, it is often referred to as the "electric distance"). If the shape of the protein–solution interface is irregular, the interaction of the solute charges with the membrane potential is more complicated than the simple linear field.

Added note: Potential across a planar membrane

To illustrate the consequences of Eq. (4.20), let us consider a simple planar membrane separating two aqueous salt solutions of concentration $[C]$. For simplicity, we consider a region of the membrane that is impermeable and contains no ion channels. The system is divided into three regions: region 1 (for $x \leq 0$) and region 3 (for $L \leq x$) are aqueous ionic solutions, and region 2 (for $0 \leq x \leq L$) is a hydrocarbon lipid membrane. The dielectric constants of water and the membrane are ϵ_w and ϵ_m, respectively. In each region, the potential obeys:

$$\phi_1''(x) = \kappa^2 \phi_1(x)$$
$$\phi_2''(x) = 0 \qquad (4.21)$$
$$\phi_3''(x) = \kappa^2 (\phi_3(x) - \Delta\phi)$$

where κ^{-1} is the Debye screening length. Note that if the membrane is impermeable, κ need not be the same on side 1 and side 3. The asymptotic boundary conditions are:

$$\phi_1(-\infty) = 0$$
$$\phi_3(+\infty) = \Delta\phi \qquad (4.22)$$

and the continuity boundary conditions are:

$$\phi_1(0) = \phi_2(0)$$
$$\epsilon_w \phi_1'(0) = \epsilon_m \phi_2'(0)$$
$$\phi_2(L) = \phi_3(L) \qquad (4.23)$$
$$\epsilon_m \phi_2'(L) = \epsilon_w \phi_3'(L)$$

The solution is

$$\phi_1(x) = A e^{\kappa x}$$
$$\phi_2(x) = A \left[\frac{\epsilon_w}{\epsilon_m} \kappa x + 1 \right] \qquad (4.24)$$
$$\phi_1(x) = \Delta\phi - A e^{-\kappa x}$$

where A is a constant equal to

$$A = \Delta\phi \left[2 + \frac{\epsilon_w}{\epsilon_m} \kappa L \right]^{-1} \qquad (4.25)$$

The potential difference at the membrane $\Delta\phi_m = \phi_2(L) - \phi_2(0)$ is

$$\Delta\phi_m = \Delta\phi \left[1 + \frac{2\epsilon_m}{\kappa L \epsilon_w} \right]^{-1} . \qquad (4.26)$$

The dielectric constant of water ϵ_w is 80, the dielectric constant of the hydrocarbon membrane ϵ_m is $\simeq 2$, in frog Ringer solution the Debye length κ^{-1} is 9 Å, and the thickness of the membrane is about 40 Å. Using these values, the membrane potential $\Delta\phi_m$ is $\simeq 0.98\Delta\phi$. This shows that the potential varies only inside the membrane. Little potential drop takes place outside the membrane because the strong electrolytic ionic solution is a "good conductor." The density of ions i on each side of the membrane is given by

$$[C_i(x)]_1 = [C_i]_1 \left(1 - \frac{q_i \phi(x)}{k_B T}\right)$$

$$[C_i(x)]_2 = [C_i]_2 \left(1 - \frac{q_i(\phi(x) - \Delta\phi)}{k_B T}\right) \tag{4.27}$$

The electrostatic free energy of a macromolecule embedded in a membrane in the presence of a membrane potential V can be expressed as the sum of three separate terms involving the capacitance C of the system, the reaction field $\Phi_{\mathrm{rf}}(\mathbf{r})$, and the membrane potential field $\phi_{\mathrm{mp}}(\mathbf{r})$:

$$\Delta W^{\mathrm{elec}} = \frac{1}{2}CV_{\mathrm{mp}}^2 + \frac{1}{2}\sum_i q_i \Phi_{\mathrm{rf}}(\mathbf{r}_i) + \left[\sum_i q_i \phi_{\mathrm{mp}}(\mathbf{r}_i)\right] V_{\mathrm{mp}} \tag{4.28}$$

where q_i and $\mathbf{r}_i$ are the charge and the distance from the macromolecule, respectively. The first term is the capacitive energy contribution, which is generally negligible. The second term is the voltage-independent reaction field contribution, which was described in Section 4.1. The third term in Eq. (4.28) represents the interaction of the macromolecule charges with the membrane potential. The quantity $\phi_{\mathrm{mp}}(\mathbf{r}_i)$ represents the fraction of the membrane potential produced by the atomic charge q_i at $\mathbf{r}_i$. In the case of a perfectly planar system (see box), the electric field across the membrane is constant and $\phi_{\mathrm{mp}}(\mathbf{r}_i)$ is simply the fraction of the membrane thickness. For this reason, it is often referred to as the "electric distance" as illustrated in Figure 4.3. If there are variations in the membrane thickness, the field from the membrane potential will be more focused in the thinner region. As illustrated in Figure 4.4, the same physical displacement by a charge is not expected to yield the same apparent fraction of the membrane potential depending on the local thickness of the membrane. The influence of the membrane potential on the energetics of charge movement is important. To the lowest order, the change in free energy when a charge moves can be expressed as $\Delta W_{\mathrm{tot}} = \Delta W_0 + qV_{\mathrm{mp}}f$, where f is the fraction of the membrane potential felt by the charge. For example, if a charge moves from the solution set at V to a site in the membrane. The interaction of the macromolecule charges with the membrane potential in Eq. (4.28) may be expressed in terms of an effective charge $\mathcal{Q}$ as,

$$\mathcal{Q} = \sum_i q_i \phi_{\mathrm{mp}}(\mathbf{r}_i) \tag{4.29}$$

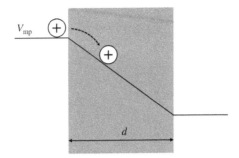

Fig. 4.3   Charge movement and membrane potential. The transmembrane electric field is linear across a uniform membrane of thickness d. In this case, the voltage drop and electric distance are directly proportional to the physical displacement of a charge within the membrane.

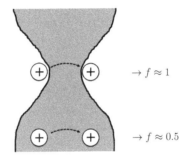

Fig. 4.4   Effect of membrane thickness on electric distance and membrane potential. Even though the physical displacement of the charge δd is the same in the two cases, the apparent electric distance based on the fraction of the membrane potential f will be roughly equal to 1 when the charge is moving in a region where the membrane is thin, but roughly equal to 0.5 (in this example) when the charge is moving in a region where the membrane is twice as thick.

The relative free energy between two conformations, a and b, of a macro-molecule, may be expressed as $\Delta \mathcal{Q}_{ab} V_{\mathrm{mp}}$, where $\Delta \mathcal{Q}_{ab} = [\mathcal{Q}_a - \mathcal{Q}_b]$ is the "gating charge." This concept is important in the study of voltage-activated membrane channels, which are activated through the movement of charged residues.

4.3   Finite-difference Poisson–Boltzmann equation

We have reviewed some of the basic aspects of ion solvation and solvent-mediated ion–ion interactions in bulk solution, and highlighted the fact

that the solvation free energy of polar systems in water is often dominated by electrostatics. The treatment of complex molecular systems of
arbitrary geometries with classical continuum electrostatic methods follows
essentially the same principles. The PB equation is a differential equation.
Numerical solution of this equation for nontrivial geometries is made possible by mapping the problem onto a three-dimensional discrete grid and
approximating the derivatives with finite-difference expression. All derivatives are expressed from finite differences. For example, for a function $f(x)$:

$$\frac{\partial f}{\partial x} = \frac{f(x + \frac{\Delta x}{2}) - f(x - \frac{\Delta x}{2})}{\Delta x} \tag{4.30}$$

In particular, the PB equation comprises terms of the type,

$$\frac{\partial}{\partial x}(\epsilon E_x) = \frac{\epsilon(x + \frac{\Delta x}{2})E_x(x + \frac{\Delta x}{2}) - \epsilon(x - \frac{\Delta x}{2})E_x(x - \frac{\Delta x}{2})}{\Delta x} \tag{4.31}$$

where E_x is the electric field along the x-direction, which itself is also related
to a derivative of the electrostatic potential $E_x = -\partial\phi/\partial x$. Therefore, the
electric field E_x at $x^* = x + \frac{\Delta x}{2}$ is

$$E(x^*)\bigg|_{x^*=x+\frac{\Delta x}{2}} = -\left(\frac{\phi(x^* + \frac{\Delta x}{2}) - \phi(x^* - \frac{\Delta x}{2})}{\Delta x}\right)\bigg|_{x^*=x+\frac{\Delta x}{2}}$$

$$= -\left[\frac{\phi(x + \Delta x) - \phi(x)}{\Delta x}\right] \tag{4.32}$$

and the electric field E_x at $x - \frac{\Delta x}{2}$ is

$$E\left(x - \frac{\Delta x}{2}\right) = -\left[\frac{\phi(x) - \phi(x - \Delta x)}{\Delta x}\right] \tag{4.33}$$

Combining these expressions in the initial equation yields:

$$\frac{\partial}{\partial x}(\epsilon E_x) = -\epsilon\left(x + \frac{\Delta x}{2}\right)\left[\frac{\phi(x + \Delta x) - \phi(x)}{\Delta x^2}\right]$$

$$+\epsilon\left(x - \frac{\Delta x}{2}\right)\left[\frac{\phi(x) - \phi(x - \Delta x)}{\Delta x^2}\right] \tag{4.34}$$

Similar expressions can be obtained for the y and z components of the
divergence. Assuming a single grid spacing $\Delta x = \Delta y = \Delta z = h$ for a cubic

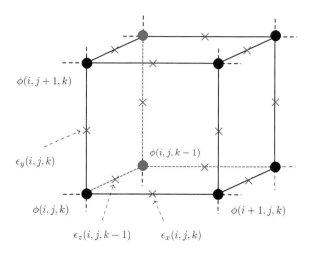

Fig. 4.5 The grid tabulating the potential and the dielectric constant at different sites. The indices i, j, and k are increasing in the right, upward, and forward directions, respectively.

lattice, we obtain the complete terms of the finite-difference,

$$
\begin{aligned}
\epsilon_x(i,j,k)[\phi(i+1,j,k) - \phi(i,j,k)] &+ \epsilon_x(i-1,j,k)[\phi(i-1,j,k) - \phi(i,j,k)] \\
+ \epsilon_y(i,j,k)[\phi(i,j+1,k) - \phi(i,j,k)] &+ \epsilon_y(i,j-1,k)[\phi(i,j-1,k) - \phi(i,j,k)] \\
+ \epsilon_z(i,j,k)[\phi(i,j,k+1) - \phi(i,j,k)] &+ \epsilon_z(i,j,k-1)[\phi(i,j,k-1) - \phi(i,j,k)] \\
- \bar{\kappa}^2(i,j,k)\phi(i,j,k)h^2 &= -4\pi\frac{q(i,j,k)}{h}
\end{aligned}
\tag{4.35}
$$

The fractional charge is related to the density at the grid points through $\rho(i,j,k) = q(i,j,k)/h^3$. A typical site on the lattice is illustrated in Figure 4.5. The main quantities that can be defined for the grid points (x_i, y_j, z_k) of the lattice are the electrostatic potential $\phi(x,y,z) \to \phi(i,j,k)$, $\bar{\kappa}(x,y,z) \to \bar{\kappa}(i,j,k)$, which is the modified Debye–Hückel screening factor, $q(x,y,z) \to q(i,j,k)$, which is the fractional charge, and the dielectric mapping on the half-distance branches $\epsilon(x + \Delta x/2) \to \epsilon_x(i)$ and $\epsilon(x - \Delta x/2) \to \epsilon_x(i-1)$. The arrays $\epsilon_x(i,j,k)$, $\epsilon_y(i,j,k)$, and $\epsilon_z(i,j,k)$ represent the dielectric constants associated with the x-, y-, and z-direction grid branches, $(x_i + h/2, y_j, z_k)$, $(x_i, y_j + h/2, z_k)$, and $(x_i, y_j, z_k + h/2)$ originating at the grid point (x_i, y_j, z_k).

The finite-difference PB Eq. (4.35) may also be expressed as a formal linear algebra problem,

$$
\mathbf{M} \cdot \vec{\phi} = -4\pi\vec{q}
\tag{4.36}
$$

where $\mathbf{M}$ is a symmetric matrix, and $\vec{\phi}$ and $\vec{q}$ are column vectors associated with the electrostatic potentials and the fractional charges, respectively, whose number of elements is equal to the number of grid points on the 3D lattice. Eq. (4.36) is interesting because its solution can be formally expressed as $\vec{\phi} = -4\pi\mathbf{M}^{-1} \cdot \vec{q}$. The charging free energy involves terms of the type,

$$\Delta G_{\text{elec}} = \frac{1}{2} \vec{q}^{\,\text{t}} \cdot \vec{\phi}$$

$$= \frac{-4\pi}{2} \vec{q}^{\,\text{t}} \cdot \mathbf{M}^{-1} \cdot \vec{q} \tag{4.37}$$

where the superscript "t" indicates the transpose of the associated vector. In principle, this can provide a closed-form expression for the charging free energy. However, $\mathbf{M}$ is an extremely large matrix that would be difficult to invert. Thus, the numerical solution is obtained through an iterative relaxation method by rewriting Eq. (4.35) as,

$$\phi(i,j,k) = 4\pi\frac{q(i,j,k)}{h}\frac{1}{\bar{\kappa}^2(i,j,k)h^2 + \sum_6 \epsilon} + \frac{\sum_6 \epsilon\phi}{\bar{\kappa}^2(i,j,k)h^2 + \sum_6 \epsilon} \tag{4.38}$$

where

$$\sum_6 \epsilon \equiv \epsilon_x(i,j,k) + \epsilon_x(i-1,j,k) + \epsilon_y(i,j,k) + \epsilon_y(i,j-1,k)$$

$$+ \epsilon_z(i,j,k) + \epsilon_z(i,j,k-1) \tag{4.39}$$

and

$$\sum_6 \epsilon\phi \equiv \epsilon_x(i,j,k)\phi(i+1,j,k) + \epsilon_x(i-1,j,k)\phi(i-1,j,k)$$

$$+ \epsilon_y(i,j,k)\phi(i,j+1,k) + \epsilon_y(i,j-1,k)\phi(i,j-1,k)$$

$$+ \epsilon_z(i,j,k)\phi(i,j,k+1) + \epsilon_z(i,j,k-1)\phi(i,j,k-1) \tag{4.40}$$

The terms involved in updating the electrostatic potential at the lattice point (i,j,k), using the half-distance branches of the dielectric function, are illustrated in Figure 4.6. Several programs are available for computing the electrostatic potential by solving the finite-difference PB equation [Warwicker and Watson (1982); Klapper *et al.* (1986); Davis *et al.* (1991); Im *et al.* (1998); Baker *et al.* (2001)].

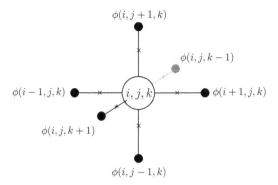

Fig. 4.6 Discrete mapping of the six nearest branches on the finite-difference lattice. The potential values ϕ are tabulated on the lattice vertices, while the dielectric constants are tabulated on the segments (marked by a $\times$), halfway between the lattice vertices. Specifically, $\epsilon_x(i,j,k)$ is between $\phi(i,j,k)$ and $\phi(i+1,j,k)$; $\epsilon_x(i-1,j,k)$ is between $\phi(i-1,j,k)$ and $\phi(i,j,k)$; $\epsilon_y(i,j,k)$ is between $\phi(i,j,k)$ and $\phi(i,j+1,k)$; $\epsilon_y(i,j-1,k)$ is between $\phi(i,j-1,k)$ and $\phi(i,j,k)$; $\epsilon_z(i,j,k)$ is between $\phi(i,j,k)$ and $\phi(i,j,k+1)$; and $\epsilon_z(i,j,k-1)$ is between $\phi(i,j,k-1)$ and $\phi(i,j,k)$.

4.4   Electrostatic solvation forces

It is of interest to obtain an expression for the forces, that is, the first derivative of the electrostatic free energy. These forces can then be used to optimize geometries and generate molecular dynamics (MD) trajectories in the presence of the dielectric continuum. The first derivative with respect to the position of atom i involves terms of the type [Im *et al.* (1998)],

$$\mathbf{F}_i^{\text{elec}} = 2\pi \frac{\partial}{\partial \mathbf{r}_i} \left[\vec{q}^{\,\text{t}} \cdot \mathbf{M}^{-1} \cdot \vec{q} \right]$$

$$= 2\pi \left[\frac{\partial \vec{q}^{\,\text{t}}}{\partial \mathbf{r}_i} \cdot \mathbf{M}^{-1} \cdot \vec{q} + \vec{q}^{\,\text{t}} \cdot \mathbf{M}^{-1} \cdot \frac{\partial \vec{q}}{\partial \mathbf{r}_i} + \vec{q}^{\,\text{t}} \cdot \frac{\partial \mathbf{M}^{-1}}{\partial \mathbf{r}_i} \cdot \vec{q} \right] \quad (4.41)$$

which can be simplified by using the identity,

$$\frac{\partial \mathbf{M}^{-1}}{\partial \mathbf{r}_i} = -\mathbf{M}^{-1} \cdot \frac{\partial \mathbf{M}}{\partial \mathbf{r}_i} \cdot \mathbf{M}^{-1} \quad (4.42)$$

and the formal solution $\vec{\phi} = -4\pi \mathbf{M}^{-1} \cdot \vec{q}$. In the limit of infinitesimal grid spacing, the forces may be expressed in terms of continuous integrals:

$$\mathbf{F}_i^{\text{elec}} = -\int_V d^3 \mathbf{r} \left[(\phi_{\text{s}} - \phi_{\text{v}}) \frac{\partial \rho}{\partial \mathbf{r}_i} + \frac{1}{8\pi} \phi_{\text{s}} \nabla \cdot \left[\frac{\partial \epsilon_{\text{s}}}{\partial \mathbf{r}_i} \nabla \phi_{\text{s}} \right] - \frac{1}{8\pi} \phi_{\text{s}}^2 \frac{\partial \bar{\kappa}^2}{\partial \mathbf{r}_i} \right]$$

$$(4.43)$$

The first term in Eq. (4.43) corresponds to the "reaction field force," the second term in Eq. (4.43) arises from the spatial variations of the dielectric constant function $\epsilon(\mathbf{r})$, and the third term arises from spatial variation of the modified Debye–Hückel screening factor $\bar{\kappa}(\mathbf{r})$.

4.5 The PB/SASA implicit model of solvation

A popular model to represent implicitly the effect of solvation on a biomolecule is,

$$\Delta W(\mathbf{r}_1, \ldots, \mathbf{r}_n) = \Delta W_{\text{np}}(\mathbf{r}_1, \ldots, \mathbf{r}_n) + \Delta W_{\text{elec}}(\mathbf{r}_1, \ldots, \mathbf{r}_n) \qquad (4.44)$$

where ΔW_{elec} is determined from the PB continuum electrostatic charging free energy while ΔW_{np} is assumed to be proportional to the SASA

$$\Delta W_{\text{np}} = \gamma \mathcal{S} \qquad (4.45)$$

Combining these two approximations together yields the PB/SASA implicit solvent model [Massova and Kollman (2000)]. It should be noted that the PB/SASA implicit solvent model differs from another approximation that also makes use of the concept of SASA based on the assumption that the *entire* solvation free energy of a solute can be expressed in terms of a linear sum of atomic contributions weighted by the partial of exposed surface area:

$$\Delta W(\mathbf{r}_1, \ldots, \mathbf{r}_n) = \sum_{i=1}^{n} \gamma_i \mathcal{S}_i(\mathbf{r}_1, \ldots, \mathbf{r}_n) \qquad (4.46)$$

where $\mathcal{S}_i(\mathbf{X})$ is the partial SASA of atom i (which depends on the solute configuration), and γ_i is an atomic free energy per unit area associated with atom i. Here, the contribution from electrostatic forces is not taken into account explicitly but is assumed to be incorporated indirectly into the empirical coefficients γ_i.

Chapter 5

Binding equilibrium

Issues of molecular recognition, involving the noncovalent association of small ligands to large macromolecules with high affinity and specificity, plays a crucial role in biology and medicinal chemistry. Computational studies can help elucidate the fundamental principles governing those issues at the molecular level. Moreover, improving our ability to screen large databases of compounds *in silico* to identify potential lead drug molecules with an accurate prediction of binding affinities could have a great impact on structure-based drug design. The main quantity of interest is the *standard equilibrium binding free energy*, $\Delta G_{eq}^{(\circ)}$. To calculate $\Delta G_{eq}^{(\circ)}$ with computer simulations, a mathematical relation has to be established between macroscopic observables and microscopic variables. The standard binding free energy is defined from the equilibrium constant by $\Delta G_{eq}^{(\circ)} = -k_B T \ln(C^{(\circ)} K_b)$, where $C^{(\circ)}$ is standard concentration, k_B is the Boltzmann constant, and T is the absolute temperature.

5.1 Phenomenology of binding

To take a specific example, let us consider a macromolecular receptor (R) in thermodynamic equilibrium with a dilute solution containing ligand molecules (L). Consider a binding reaction:

$$\text{R} + \text{L} \underset{}{\overset{K_b}{\rightleftharpoons}} \text{RL}$$

which is controlled by the equilibrium constant K_b,

$$K_b = \frac{[RL]}{[R][L]} \tag{5.1}$$

where [L], [R], and [RL], are the equilibrium concentrations of the unbound ligand, unbound protein, and bound complex, respectively. We assume that there is enough space only for a single ligand occupying the binding pocket of the receptor. The implication is that there can either be zero or one ligand in the binding pockets.

To make progress, it is useful to consider the problem from the point of view of the recepter. The total number of receptors in the system is the sum of receptors with zero or one ligand bound, $[R_{\text{total}}] = [R] + [RL]$. Using this constraint, it is easy to write the fraction of receptors with a bound ligand,

$$\mathcal{P}_1 = \frac{[RL]}{[R_{\text{total}}]}$$

$$= \frac{K_{\text{b}}[L]}{1 + K_{\text{b}}[L]} \tag{5.2}$$

and the fraction of receptors with no bound ligand,

$$\mathcal{P}_0 = 1 - \mathcal{P}_1$$

$$= \frac{1}{1 + K_{\text{b}}[L]} \tag{5.3}$$

and the equilibrium binding constant,

$$K_{\text{b}} = \frac{1}{[L]} \left(\frac{\mathcal{P}_1}{\mathcal{P}_0} \right) \tag{5.4}$$

We will return to this expression in Section 5.3 to formulate a microscopic statistical theory of binding. First-order binding is often reported in terms of the dissociation constant:

$$K_{\text{D}} = \frac{1}{K_{\text{b}}} \tag{5.5}$$

which is typically given in units of concentration. In the biological sciences, it is most common to convey information about binding affinities in terms of a dissociation constant. As illustrated in Figure 5.1, K_{D} is the concentration at which the probability of occupancy $\mathcal{P}_1$ is equal to one-half:

$$\mathcal{P}_1 = \frac{K_{\text{b}}[L]}{1 + K_{\text{b}}[L]}$$

$$= \frac{\frac{[L]}{K_{\text{D}}}}{1 + \frac{[L]}{K_{\text{D}}}} \tag{5.6}$$

when $[L] = K_{\text{D}}$, then $\mathcal{P}_1 = 0.5$.

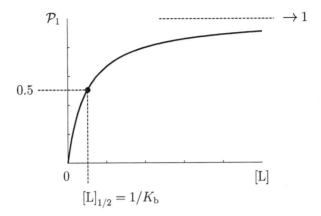

Fig. 5.1 Probability $\mathcal{P}_1$ from Eq. (5.6) that the binding site is occupied by a ligand as a function of ligand concentration.

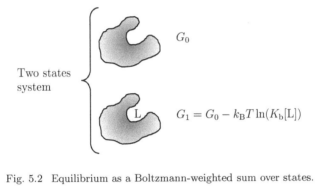

Fig. 5.2 Equilibrium as a Boltzmann-weighted sum over states.

5.2 Equilibrium as a Boltzmann-weighted sum over states

In treating equilibrium binding and constructing all the occupancy probabilities, it is sometimes useful to imagine discrete concentration-dependent free energy shifts between states. The discrete states with their respective free energy are illustrated in Figure 5.2. In this manner, the occupancy probabilities may be expressed as,

$$
\mathcal{P}_1 = \frac{e^{-G_1/k_BT}}{e^{-G_0/k_BT} + e^{-G_1/k_BT}}
$$

$$
= \frac{e^{-[G_0 - k_BT\ln(K_b[L])]/k_BT}}{e^{-G_0/k_BT} + e^{-[G_0 - k_BT\ln(K_b[L])]/k_BT}}
$$

$$
= \frac{e^{-G_0/k_BT}}{e^{-G_0/k_BT}} \times \frac{K_b[L]}{1 + K_b[L]} \tag{5.7}
$$

Likewise, the occupancy probabilities for models with a large number of discrete states can simply be expressed as Boltzmann-weighted states:

$$\mathcal{P}_i = \frac{e^{-G_i/k_{\mathrm{B}}T}}{\sum_{\text{state } i} e^{-G_i/k_{\mathrm{B}}T}} \tag{5.8}$$

This approach is useful when we construct extensive multistate models of complex biomolecular systems such as ion pumps, membrane transporters, and so on (see Chapter 12).

5.3 Microscopic treatment and statistical mechanical expression

Assuming that there are no interferences between receptors, an equivalent equilibrium situation corresponds to that of a single receptor surrounded by a solution of ligands at concentration $[L]$ (Figure 5.3). In this case, the fraction of receptors with or without a bound ligand is equivalent to the probability of a single receptor to adopt this state. Starting from Eq. (5.4) to obtain an appropriate expression for the equilibrium binding constant, we consider,

$$\frac{\mathcal{P}_1}{\mathcal{P}_0} = \left(\frac{\text{number of configurations with one bound ligand}}{\text{number of configurations with no bound ligand}}\right) \tag{5.9}$$

where we assumed that, at the most, one ligand at a given time can bind to the receptor (though it is possible to generalize the present treatment to allow multiple occupancy).

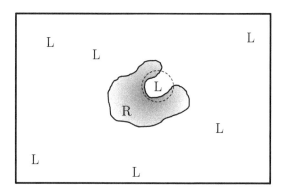

Fig. 5.3 A single isolated protein receptor is in thermodynamic equilibrium with a solution of ligand L, which can reversibly associate with a binding site. For the sake of simplicity, we assume that the protein receptor can freely move, but that its center-of-mass is fixed at the origin and its orientation is fixed (without tumbling). There are N ligands in the solution of volume V for a concentration $[L] = N/V$. The translation and rotation of the protein (with or without bound ligand) has no influence on the final result and can be removed from the present considerations.

Now, we have to translate the ratio on the r.h.s. or Eq. (5.9) into a ratio of statistical mechanical configuration integrals. Let the coordinates of the ligand i be represented by where $\mathbf{L}_i$ and the coordinates of the remaining atoms (receptor and solvent) represented by $\mathbf{Y}$. In principle, in determining the number of configurations with one bound ligand, the binding site could be occupied by ligand 1, or ligand 2, or any of the N ligands present in the system. As all the ligands are identical, it is possible to pick ligand 1 and multiply the expression by N to correctly account for all the possible configurations with one bound ligand. This yields:

$$\frac{\mathcal{P}_1}{\mathcal{P}_0} = N \; \frac{\int_{\text{site}} d\mathbf{L}_1 \int_{\text{bulk}} d\mathbf{L}_2 \cdots \int_{\text{bulk}} d\mathbf{L}_N \int d\mathbf{Y} \, e^{-U/k_{\text{B}}T}}{\int_{\text{bulk}} d\mathbf{L}_1 \int_{\text{bulk}} d\mathbf{L}_2 \cdots \int_{\text{bulk}} d\mathbf{L}_N \int d\mathbf{Y} \, e^{-U/k_{\text{B}}T}}, \tag{5.10}$$

where it was assumed that there is no translational and tumbling movement of the macromolecular receptor. In the numerator, ligand molecule number 1 has been chosen to occupy the binding site while the remaining ligands are constrained to remain in the bulk solution. The factor of N is included to account for the multiple ways to obtain equivalent configurations by choosing any of the N identical ligand to occupy the binding site. The subscript "site" on the integrals implies that the position of the center-of-mass of the ligand is restricted to be inside some predefined spatial region that we ascribe to the binding site. Correspondingly, the subscript "bulk" on the integrals implies that the position of the center-of-mass of the ligand is in the bulk solution. The other ligands that are far away in solution do not interact with the protein, and their influence may be neglected. For this reason, the integration of the ligands $2, \ldots, N$ located in the bulk solution, which appear in both the numerator and denominator can be factored out, leaving,

$$K_{\text{b}} = \frac{1}{[L]} \left(\frac{\mathcal{P}_1}{\mathcal{P}_0} \right) = \frac{1}{[L]} \times N \; \frac{\int_{\text{site}} d\mathbf{L} \; \int d\mathbf{Y} \, e^{-U/k_{\text{B}}T}}{\int_{\text{bulk}} d\mathbf{L} \; \int d\mathbf{Y} \, e^{-U/k_{\text{B}}T}} \tag{5.11}$$

(From here on, we will drop the subscript 1 on the ligand's number of degrees of freedom $\mathbf{L}_1$ for the sake of simplicity.) Now let us introduce a factor of unity, $1 = \int d\mathbf{r}' \, \delta(\mathbf{r}_{\mathbf{L}} - \mathbf{r}')$, inside the integrals, where $\mathbf{r}_{\mathbf{L}}$ represents the position of the center-of-mass of the ligand,

$$K_{\text{b}} = \frac{1}{[L]} \times N \; \frac{\int_{\text{site}} d\mathbf{r}' \int d\mathbf{L} \, \delta(\mathbf{r}_{\mathbf{L}} - \mathbf{r}') \int d\mathbf{Y} \, e^{-U/k_{\text{B}}T}}{\int_{\text{bulk}} d\mathbf{r}'' \int d\mathbf{L} \, \delta(\mathbf{r}_{\mathbf{L}} - \mathbf{r}'') \int d\mathbf{Y} \, e^{-U/k_{\text{B}}T}}$$

$$= \frac{1}{[L]} \times N \; \frac{\int_{\text{site}} d\mathbf{r}' \, e^{-W(\mathbf{r}')/k_{\text{B}}T}}{\int_{\text{bulk}} d\mathbf{r}'' \, e^{-W(\mathbf{r}'')/k_{\text{B}}T}} \tag{5.12}$$

Here, we have defined the potential mean force (PMF) for the ligand's center-of-mass,

$$e^{-W(\mathbf{r}')/k_{\mathrm{B}}T} \propto \int d\mathbf{L} \; \delta(\mathbf{r_L} - \mathbf{r}') \int d\mathbf{Y} \, e^{-U/k_{\mathrm{B}}T} \tag{5.13}$$

In the bulk region, the PMF is a constant when the ligand is far away from the receptor. That is, $W(\mathbf{r}'') = W_{\mathrm{bulk}}$ when $\mathbf{r}'' \in$ bulk. This enables us to further simplify the expression for the equilibrium binding constant,

$$K_{\mathrm{b}} = \frac{1}{[L]} \times N \; \frac{\int_{\mathrm{site}} d\mathbf{r}' \, e^{-W(\mathbf{r}')/k_{\mathrm{B}}T}}{e^{-W_{\mathrm{bulk}}/k_{\mathrm{B}}T} \underbrace{\int_{\mathrm{bulk}} d\mathbf{r}''}_{=V}}$$

$$= \frac{1}{[L]} \times \frac{N}{N} \int_{\mathrm{site}} d\mathbf{r}' \, e^{-[W(\mathbf{r}')-W_{\mathrm{bulk}}]/k_{\mathrm{B}}T}$$

$$= \int_{\mathrm{site}} d\mathbf{r}' \, e^{-[W(\mathbf{r}')-W_{\mathrm{bulk}}]/k_{\mathrm{B}}T} \tag{5.14}$$

where the translational integral of the ligand over the entire volume of the bulk solution has been expressed explicitly (the factor V is in the denominator). A first observation is that binding is largely controlled by the difference in free energy or PMF between the solution and the binding site. A second observation is that the equilibrium constant K_{b} has the dimension of volume (e.g., Å^3) because of the extra translational integral over $\mathbf{r}$ in the numerator but not in the denominator (the translational integral of the ligand over the entire volume of the bulk solution was expressed explicitly to cancel the ligand concentration). For example, if the ligand can bind uniformly inside a small microscopic volume ΔV_{site} with a constant free energy $\Delta W \equiv [W_{\mathrm{site}} - W_{\mathrm{bulk}}]$, then the binding constant is simply:

$$K_{\mathrm{b}} \approx \Delta V_{\mathrm{site}} \, e^{-\Delta W/k_{\mathrm{B}}T} \tag{5.15}$$

The quantity ΔW represents the interaction free energy between the ligand and the receptor.

5.4 Translating binding free energy into interaction

In chemistry, binding constants measured experimentally are typically reported in inverse concentration, $\mathrm{M}^{-1}(\equiv \mathrm{mole/liter})^{-1}$ (although the biological literature predominantly uses the dissociation constant K_D expressed in M). Traditionally, one translates K_b into the standard equilibrium binding free energy $\Delta G_{eq}^{(\circ)}$ by assuming the standard concentration $C^{(\circ)}$ of 1 M, $\Delta G_{eq}^{(\circ)} = -k_B T \ln[K_b C^{(\circ)}]$. But our statistical mechanical expression Eq. (5.14), which yields K_b in Å^3 for the microscopic model, needs to be converted to M^{-1}. The conversion factor is Avogadro's number divided by the number of Å^3 in a liter,

$$K_b \text{ in } M^{-1} = \frac{6.02 \times 10^{23}/\text{mole}}{10^{27} \text{Å}^3/\text{liter}} \times \left(\int_{\text{site}} d\mathbf{r}' \, e^{-[W(\mathbf{r}') - W_{\text{bulk}}]/k_B T} \text{ in } \text{Å}^3 \right)$$

$$= \frac{1}{1661} \frac{M^{-1}}{\text{Å}^3} \times \left(\int_{\text{site}} d\mathbf{r}' \, e^{-[W(\mathbf{r}') - W_{\text{bulk}}]/k_B T} \text{ in } \text{Å}^3 \right) \quad (5.16)$$

This clarifies the meaning of the standard equilibrium binding free energy $\Delta G_{eq}^{(\circ)}$. For example, in the case of a ligand binding uniformly inside a small volume ΔV_{site} given by Eq. (5.15),

$$\Delta G_{eq}^{(\circ)} = -k_B T \ln \left(\frac{1}{1661} \frac{M^{-1}}{\text{Å}^3} \times \Delta V_{\text{site}} \, e^{-\Delta W/k_B T} \, \text{Å}^3 \times C^{(\circ)} \right)$$

$$= \Delta W - k_B T \ln \left(\frac{\Delta V_{\text{site}} \text{ in } \text{Å}^3}{1661} \right) \quad (5.17)$$

Assuming the microscopic volume ΔV_{site} of $1\,\text{Å}^3$, the standard binding free energy $\Delta G_{eq}^{(\circ)}$ is equal to $\Delta W + 4.42\,\text{kcal/mol}$. Clearly, $\Delta G_{eq}^{(\circ)}$ is not equal to the average interaction free energy ΔW between the ligand and the receptor. In this example, there is an extra unfavorable free energy of $4.42\,\text{kcal/mol}$. For a microscopic volume of $1\,\text{Å}^3$, dissociation constants K_D of $1\,\text{nM}$, $1\,\mu\text{M}$, and $1\,\text{mM}$, yield free energy interactions ΔW equal to -16.6, -12.6, and $-8.5\,\text{kcal/mol}$, respectively.

5.5 Alchemical free energy perturbation approach

The above treatment culminating with Eq. (5.14) offers useful insight into the microscopic ingredients that underlies the concept of the equilibrium constant. This PMF-based treatment also provides a powerful route to calculate the equilibrium constant of a ligand binding to a receptor on the basis of the ligand–receptor PMF, $W(\mathbf{r})$ [Deng and Roux (2008)].

An alternative computational route to K_b, which is widely used in the field of computer-aided drug design (CADD), is presented by alchemical free energy perturbation (FEP) simulations. Returning to Eq. (5.11), we first rewrite K_b as,

$$
\begin{aligned}
K_b &= \frac{1}{[L]} \times N \ \frac{\int_{\text{site}} d\mathbf{L} \int d\mathbf{Y}\, e^{-U/k_B T}}{\int_{\text{bulk}} d\mathbf{r}' \int d\mathbf{L} \int d\mathbf{Y}\, \delta(\mathbf{r_L} - \mathbf{r}')\, e^{-U/k_B T}} \\[2mm]
&= \frac{1}{[L]} \times N \ \frac{\int_{\text{site}} d\mathbf{L} \int d\mathbf{Y}\, e^{-U/k_B T}}{V \int d\mathbf{L} \int d\mathbf{Y}\, \delta(\mathbf{r_L} - \mathbf{r}_{\text{bulk}})\, e^{-U/k_B T}} \\[2mm]
&= \frac{\int_{\text{site}} d\mathbf{L} \int d\mathbf{Y}\, e^{-U/k_B T}}{\int d\mathbf{L} \int d\mathbf{Y}\, \delta(\mathbf{r_L} - \mathbf{r}_{\text{bulk}})\, e^{-U/k_B T}}
\end{aligned}
\tag{5.18}
$$

The delta function in the denominator implies that the center-of-mass of the ligand, $\mathbf{r_L}$, is held fixed at some point, $\mathbf{r}_{\text{bulk}}$, in the bulk solution. A useful strategy for computing the equilibrium constant introduced in Chapter 3 is to rely on the concept of artificial potential energy function, U^*, in which the ligand is completely decoupled from its environment (receptor and solvent). For convenience, we will also stage in a translational restraining potential acting on the center-of-mass of the ligand $u_t(\mathbf{r_L})$ relative to the binding site to prevent the decoupled ligand from wandering in the simulation system (with potential energy U^*). As in Section 3.2, we multiply the expression for the equilibrium binding constant by 1,

$$
\begin{aligned}
K_b &= \frac{\int_{\text{site}} d\mathbf{L} \int d\mathbf{Y}\, e^{-U/k_B T}}{\int d\mathbf{L} \int d\mathbf{Y}\, \delta(\mathbf{r_L} - \mathbf{r}_{\text{bulk}})\, e^{-U/k_B T}} \times 1 \\[2mm]
&= \int_{\text{site}} d\mathbf{L} \int d\mathbf{Y}\, e^{-U/k_B T} \\[2mm]
&\quad \times \left(\frac{\int_{\text{site}} d\mathbf{L} \int d\mathbf{Y}\, e^{-[U+u_t]/k_B T}}{\int_{\text{site}} d\mathbf{L} \int d\mathbf{Y}\, e^{-[U+u_t]/k_B T}} \right. \\[2mm]
&\qquad\quad \frac{\int_{\text{site}} d\mathbf{L} \int d\mathbf{Y}\, e^{-[U^*+u_t]/k_B T}}{\int_{\text{site}} d\mathbf{L} \int d\mathbf{Y}\, e^{-[U^*+u_t]/k_B T}} \\[2mm]
&\qquad\quad \left. \frac{\int_{\text{bulk}} d\mathbf{L} \int d\mathbf{Y}\, \delta(\mathbf{r_L} - \mathbf{r})\, e^{-U^*/k_B T}}{\int_{\text{bulk}} d\mathbf{L} \int d\mathbf{Y}\, \delta(\mathbf{r_L} - \mathbf{r})\, e^{-U^*/k_B T}} \right) \\[2mm]
&\quad \times \frac{1}{\int d\mathbf{L} \int d\mathbf{Y}\, \delta(\mathbf{r_L} - \mathbf{r}_{\text{bulk}})\, e^{-U/k_B T}}
\end{aligned}
\tag{5.19}
$$

to get the expression,

$$K_b = \frac{\int_{\text{site}} d\mathbf{L} \int d\mathbf{Y} \, e^{-U/k_B T}}{\int_{\text{site}} d\mathbf{L} \int d\mathbf{Y} \, e^{-[U+u_t]/k_B T}}$$

$$\times \frac{\int_{\text{site}} d\mathbf{L} \int d\mathbf{Y} \, e^{-[U+u_t]/k_B T}}{\int_{\text{site}} d\mathbf{L} \int d\mathbf{Y} \, e^{-[U^*+u_t]/k_B T}}$$

$$\times \frac{\int_{\text{site}} d\mathbf{L} \int d\mathbf{Y} \, e^{-[U^*+u_t]/k_B T}}{\int_{\text{bulk}} d\mathbf{L} \int d\mathbf{Y} \, \delta(\mathbf{r_L} - \mathbf{r}) \, e^{-U^*/k_B T}}$$

$$\times \frac{\int_{\text{bulk}} d\mathbf{L} \int d\mathbf{Y} \, \delta(\mathbf{r_L} - \mathbf{r}) \, e^{-U^*/k_B T}}{\int_{\text{bulk}} d\mathbf{L} \int d\mathbf{Y} \, \delta(\mathbf{r_L} - \mathbf{r}_{\text{bulk}}) \, e^{-U/k_B T}} \qquad (5.20)$$

To rewrite this expression in a more compact form, it is useful to define the translation factor,

$$F_t = \frac{\int_{\text{site}} d\mathbf{L} \int d\mathbf{Y} \, e^{-[U^*+u_t]/k_B T}}{\int_{\text{bulk}} d\mathbf{L} \int d\mathbf{Y} \, \delta(\mathbf{r_L} - \mathbf{r}) \, e^{-U^*/k_B T}}$$

$$= \frac{\int d\mathbf{L} \int d\mathbf{Y} \, e^{-[U^*+u_t]/k_B T}}{\int d\mathbf{L} \int d\mathbf{Y} \, \delta(\mathbf{r_L} - \mathbf{r}) \, e^{-U^*/kBT}}$$

$$= \int d\mathbf{r_L} \, e^{-u_t(\mathbf{r_L})/k_B T} \qquad (5.21)$$

which has dimensions of volume (note that the center-of-mass of the decoupled ligand $\mathbf{r_L}$ can be arbitrarily translated). Other terms are simple relative free energies that can be defined as,

$$e^{-\beta \Delta G_t} = \frac{\int_{\text{site}} d\mathbf{L} \int d\mathbf{Y} \, e^{-[U+u_t]/k_B T}}{\int_{\text{site}} d\mathbf{L} \int d\mathbf{Y} \, e^{-U/k_B T}} \qquad (5.22)$$

$$e^{-\beta \Delta G_{\text{site}}} = \frac{\int_{\text{site}} d\mathbf{L} \int d\mathbf{Y} \, e^{-[U+u_t]/k_B T}}{\int_{\text{site}} d\mathbf{L} \int d\mathbf{Y} \, e^{-[U^*+u_t]/k_B T}} \qquad (5.23)$$

and

$$e^{-\beta \Delta G_{\text{bulk}}} = \frac{\int_{\text{bulk}} d\mathbf{L} \, \delta(\mathbf{r_L} - \mathbf{r}_{\text{bulk}}) \int d\mathbf{Y} \, e^{-U/k_B T}}{\int_{\text{bulk}} d\mathbf{L} \, \delta(\mathbf{r_L} - \mathbf{r}_{\text{bulk}}) \int d\mathbf{Y} \, e^{-U^*/k_B T}} \qquad (5.24)$$

where we have substituted $\mathbf{r}$ by $\mathbf{r}_{\text{bulk}}$ in the numerator, as the bulk solution region is invariant by translation. This last term is essentially the solvation free energy of the ligand in the bulk solvent that was previously defined in Eq. (3.7). It follows that the equilibrium binding constant is

$$K_b = e^{\Delta G_t/k_B T} \, F_t \, e^{-[\Delta G_{site} - \Delta G_{bulk}]/k_B T} \tag{5.25}$$

This expression was obtained in the presence of the restraining potential u_t. In practice, it can be expected that the convergence will be optimal if the form of the potential is chosen to best-match the configurational freedom of the ligand in the interacting system with potential energy U. For a simple harmonic potential centered on $\mathbf{r}_{ref}$ with force constant k_t,

$$u_t(\mathbf{r_L}) = \frac{1}{2} k_t (\mathbf{r_L} - \mathbf{r}_{ref})^2 \tag{5.26}$$

an appropriate choice to take might be that the position $\mathbf{r}_{ref}$ corresponds to the average position of the center-of-mass of the ligand in the binding site,

$$\mathbf{r}_{ref} = \langle \mathbf{r_L} \rangle_{site}, \tag{5.27}$$

and use the harmonic force constant that corresponds to the fluctuations,

$$k_t = \frac{3k_B T}{\langle (\mathbf{r_L} - \langle \mathbf{r_L} \rangle)^2 \rangle} \tag{5.28}$$

In this case, $F_t = (2\pi k_B T / k_t)^{3/2}$.

The relation of this alchemical FEP-based treatment to Eqs. (5.14) and (5.15) can be formally established by considering together the net contribution associated with the translation of the ligand, ΔG_t and F_t,

$$
\begin{aligned}
e^{\beta \Delta G_t} \, F_t &= \frac{\int_{site} d(\mathbf{L}) \int d\mathbf{Y} \, e^{-U/k_B T}}{\int_{site} d(\mathbf{L}) \int d\mathbf{Y} \, e^{-[U+u_t]/k_B T}} \times \int d\mathbf{r_L} \, e^{-\beta u_t(\mathbf{r_L})} \\
&= \frac{\int_{site} d\mathbf{r_L} \, e^{-W(\mathbf{r_L})/k_B T}}{\int_{site} d\mathbf{r_L} \, e^{-W(\mathbf{r_L})/k_B T} e^{-u_t(\mathbf{r_L})/k_B T}} \times \int d\mathbf{r_L} \, e^{-u_t(\mathbf{r_L})/k_B T} \\
&= \int_{site} d\mathbf{r_L} \, e^{-W(\mathbf{r_L})/k_B T} \times \left(\frac{\int_{site} d\mathbf{r_L} \, e^{-W(\mathbf{r_L})/k_B T} e^{-u_t(\mathbf{r_L})/k_B T}}{\int d\mathbf{r_L} \, e^{-u_t(\mathbf{r_L})/k_B T}} \right)^{-1} \\
&\approx \int_{site} d\mathbf{r_L} \, e^{-W(\mathbf{r_L})/k_B T} \times \left(e^{-W(\mathbf{r}_{ref})/k_B T} \right)^{-1} \\
&\approx \int_{site} d\mathbf{r_L} \, e^{-[W(\mathbf{r_L}) - W(\mathbf{r}_{ref})]/k_B T} \\
&\approx \Delta V_{site} \tag{5.30}
\end{aligned}
$$

with

$$K_\mathrm{b} = \Delta V_\mathrm{site}\, e^{-[\Delta G_\mathrm{site} - \Delta G_\mathrm{bulk}]/k_\mathrm{B}T} \tag{5.31}$$

where $\Delta G_\mathrm{site} = W_\mathrm{site}$ and $\Delta G_\mathrm{bulk} = W_\mathrm{bulk}$, by identification with Eqs. (5.14) and (5.15). This shows that conceptual elements such as the microscopic volume ΔV_site and the free energy difference of the ligand between the site and the bulk solvent are also present in the treatment of the equilibrium binding constant based on the alchemical FEP route. This demonstrates the formal equivalence of the alchemical FEP route with a PMF route in the computation of the equilibrium binding constant. In closing this section, it is worth noting that we have limited our discussion to a simple translational restraining potential acting on the center-of-mass of the ligand $u_\mathrm{t}(\mathbf{r_L})$ relative to the binding site. These ideas may be extended considerably by introducing in the FEP calculations a variety of extra potentials affecting the orientation of the ligand, the conformation of the ligand, and the conformation of the receptor [Deng and Roux (2009)].

Chapter 6

Dynamics and time correlation functions

So far we have mainly considered averages like $\langle x \rangle$ or $\langle x^2 \rangle$, $\langle v \rangle$ or $\langle v^2 \rangle$. Equilibrium properties of complex molecular systems can be analyzed and understood on the basis of the Maxwell–Boltzmann distribution. But different tools and concepts must be introduced to tackle time-dependent kinetic and dynamical properties, where timescales become important. One of the most important concepts in the theoretical treatment of dynamical properties is that of time-correlation functions. For example, the time-correlation function $C(t) = \langle v(t)v(0) \rangle$, represents the average of the velocity v at time 0 and the velocity at another time t. This type of joint average at two different times reports information about the system that is inherently dynamical. We will see that time-correlation functions play a critical role in the theoretical formulation of dynamical properties.

6.1 Relaxation of a nonequilibrium system

Let us consider a reference system with Hamiltonian $\mathcal{H} = \mathcal{H}_0 + A$ that has been in a state of thermodynamic equilibrium for a very long time. Let $\mathbf{\Gamma}$ represent the state of the system (coordinates and momenta). The implication is that the probability of the system to be in any state $\mathbf{\Gamma}$ is the Maxwell–Boltzmann distribution at temperature T

$$P(\mathbf{\Gamma}) = \frac{e^{-\mathcal{H}(\mathbf{\Gamma})/k_B T}}{\int d\mathbf{\Gamma}\, e^{-\mathcal{H}(\mathbf{\Gamma})/k_B T}} \tag{6.1}$$

Suddenly, at the point in time $t = 0$, the contribution A is turned off and from then on, the system simply evolves according to the classical equation of motion for the Hamiltonian $\mathcal{H}_0$. Assuming the initial condition $\mathbf{\Gamma}'$ at $t = 0$, the system dynamically evolves to $\mathbf{\Gamma}$ at a later time t through the dynamical propagation governed by the unperturbed Hamiltonian $\mathcal{H}_0$,

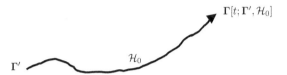

This representation of the dynamical propagation is valid for any function B expressed in terms of the variable $\mathbf{\Gamma}$, such that at time t we have,

$$B(t) = B\Big(\mathbf{\Gamma}[t; \mathbf{\Gamma}', \mathcal{H}_0]\Big) \tag{6.2}$$

where the notation is meant to remind us that the dynamical propagation is governed by the unperturbed Hamiltonian $\mathcal{H}_0$ from the initial starting point $\mathbf{\Gamma}'$ at $t = 0$. This means that the average of $B(t)$ may be expressed essentially as a Boltzmann average over the initial condition $\mathbf{\Gamma}'$,

$$\langle B(t)\rangle = \frac{\int d\mathbf{\Gamma}'\, B\Big(\mathbf{\Gamma}[t; \mathbf{\Gamma}', \mathcal{H}_0]\Big)\, e^{-\mathcal{H}(\mathbf{\Gamma}')/k_\mathrm{B}T}}{\int d\mathbf{\Gamma}\, e^{-\mathcal{H}/k_\mathrm{B}T}} \tag{6.3}$$

Let us now assume that A was actually a small perturbation and that the initial equilibrium properties of the system can be expressed in terms of the reference Hamiltonian $\mathcal{H}_0$. In Section 2.4 of Chapter 2, we derived Eq. (2.25) in the case of a small perturbation in an equilibrium average. The same expression can be used to represent the average of $B(t)$ after the time $t = 0$,

$$\langle B(t)\rangle = \langle B\rangle_0 - \frac{1}{k_\mathrm{B}T}\langle \delta B(t)\, \delta A(0)\rangle_0 \tag{6.4}$$

where the subscript 0 on the brackets $\langle \ldots \rangle_0$ means that averages are calculated with the Hamiltonian of the unperturbed equilibrium system $\mathcal{H}_0$,

$$\langle \ldots \rangle_0 = \frac{\int d\mathbf{\Gamma}\, \ldots\, e^{-\mathcal{H}_0(\mathbf{\Gamma})/k_\mathrm{B}T}}{\int d\mathbf{\Gamma}\, e^{-\mathcal{H}_0(\mathbf{\Gamma})/k_\mathrm{B}T}} \tag{6.5}$$

and

$$\delta B(t) = B(t) - \langle B\rangle_0 \tag{6.6}$$

and

$$\delta A(t) = A(t) - \langle A\rangle_0 \tag{6.7}$$

represent the deviation of A and B. This analysis shows that the average response for the relaxation of the system involves the time-correlation function $C(t)$ of the deviations δB and δA in the reference system $\mathcal{H}_0$,

$$C(t) = \langle \delta B(t)\, \delta A(0) \rangle_0 \qquad (6.8)$$

The response of the system is expressed in terms of a time-correlation function that is calculated for an equilibrium reference system governed by Hamiltonian $\mathcal{H}_0$. Because equilibrium is a state that is assumed to have existed for a very long time, the statistical properties of the fluctuations underlying the time-correlation functions are said to be stationary. By definition, a process is stationary if its statistical properties do not depend on the origin of time. In other words, what is chosen as the origin of time is unimportant and arbitrary. By virtue of stationarity, the time-correlation function of two functions $\delta B(t + t')$ and $\delta A(t)$ is

$$\begin{aligned}
C(t) &= \langle \delta B(t + t')\delta A(t') \rangle_0 \\
&= \langle \delta B(t)\delta A(0) \rangle_0 \\
&= \langle \delta B(0)\delta A(-t) \rangle_0 \qquad (6.9)
\end{aligned}$$

because the result must remain unchanged if we set $t' \to 0$, or $t' \to -t$.

One is often interested in the rate of change of the variable $B(t)$ in response to the nonequilibrium perturbation. This involves the derivative of $C(t)$ with respect to t, which can be expressed as,

$$\dot{C}(t) = \langle \delta \dot{B}(t)\delta A(0) \rangle_0 \qquad (6.10)$$

By virtue of Eq. (6.9).

$$\begin{aligned}
\frac{d}{dt'}C(t) &= 0 \\
&= \langle \delta \dot{B}(t + t')\delta A(t') \rangle_0 + \langle \delta B(t + t')\delta \dot{A}(t') \rangle_0 \qquad (6.11)
\end{aligned}$$

we also have

$$\dot{C}(t) = -\langle \delta B(t)\delta \dot{A}(0) \rangle_0 \qquad (6.12)$$

When $A = B$, then the time-correlation function is even, $C(t) = C(-t)$, and its time derivative is odd, $\dot{C}(t) = -\dot{C}(-t)$.

Once the perturbation A is removed at $t = 0$, a nonequilibrium situation is created. While the system should ultimately return to equilibrium after a macroscopically long time (e.g., ms to s), it is expected to rapidly settle into a quasi steady-state regime within some microscopic timescale τ_m (e.g., ps to μs). This quasi steady-state shall persist for a macroscopically long timescale, until the nonequilibrium state has entirely dissipated. For this reason, it is of interest to determine the rate of change in the observable $B(t)$ after the system has settled into a quasi steady-state regime in the limit that t is larger than τ_m,

$$\lim_{t \gg \tau_m} \frac{d}{dt} \langle B(t) \rangle = \lim_{t \gg \tau_m} -\frac{1}{k_B T} \dot{C}(t) \tag{6.13}$$

Ultimately, we shall assume that t can be extended to an arbitrarily long time. In practical terms, this poses no formal problem, as long as it is understood that, while t must be larger than any microscopic relaxation timescale τ_m, it must remain smaller than the macroscopic relaxation time of the complete finite system.

It is useful to convert the derivative of the time-correlation function Eq. (6.13) into the following integral form,

$$\dot{C}(t) = \left\langle \left[\delta B(0) + \int_0^t \delta \dot{B}(t') dt' \right] \delta \dot{A}(0) \right\rangle_0$$
$$= \langle \delta B(0)\, \delta \dot{A}(0) \rangle_0 + \int_0^t dt'\, \langle \delta \dot{B}(t')\, \delta \dot{A}(0) \rangle_0 \tag{6.14}$$

This expression shows that the quasi steady-state rate of change in the observable B in the nonequilibrium system is related to the integral of the time-correlation function of the time derivative of δB and δA.

6.2   Diffusion and Fick's law

As a concrete example of this type of analysis, it is instructive to examine the nonequilibrium relaxation of a dilute solution under a concentration gradient. As in Section 6.1, we begin with an unperturbed system with Hamiltonian $\mathcal{H}_0$, which is used as reference. In this unperturbed reference system, the concentration of the solute, $\overline{C} = N/V$, is uniform. To establish a concentration gradient in the initial equilibrium state of the system at $t < 0$, we introduce a perturbation of the form:

$$A = \sum_i x_i\, F_{\text{ext}} \tag{6.15}$$

where $-F_{\text{ext}}$ is a constant external force and x_i represents the coordinate of the i-th solute particle. Such a perturbation serves to initially prepare the system with the concentration profile $C(x)$ for the solute particles,

$$C(x) = \overline{C} \, e^{-x F_{\text{ext}}/k_B T} \qquad (6.16)$$

If the external force F_{ext} is small, that is, $F_{\text{ext}} x/k_B T \ll 1$ throughout the system, a linear concentration gradient is established,

$$\frac{\partial C(x)}{\partial x} \approx \frac{-1}{k_B T} \overline{C} \, F_{\text{ext}} \qquad (6.17)$$

to first order in F_{ext}. The observable that we need to follow after the perturbation is removed at $t = 0$ is the net flux of solute particles going in the x-direction, for example, the number of solute particles crossing the plane at $x = 0$ per unit of time divided by the cross-sectional area S of the system (a positive flux J is defined by an increase in the number of solute particles located on the right of the dividing surface). The progression of the system is illustrated in Figure 6.1. The instantaneous number of solute particles $\mathcal{N}(t)$ located on the right of the dividing surface $x = 0$ is

$$\mathcal{N}(t) = \sum_i H[x_i(t)] \qquad (6.18)$$

where $H(x)$ is a Heaviside indicator step-function equal to 1, when $x \geq 0$, and 0, when $x < 0$. We introduced a similar indicator function in Eq. (3.2) to analyse the solvation free energy. We seek to determine the quasi steady-state diffusion flux J_{diff} that is rapidly established after $t = 0$:

$$J_{\text{diff}} = \frac{1}{S} \lim_{t \gg \tau_m} \frac{d}{dt} \langle \mathcal{N}(t) \rangle \qquad (6.19)$$

where

$$\frac{d}{dt} \langle \mathcal{N}(t) \rangle = \frac{1}{k_B T} \langle \delta \mathcal{N}(0) \, \delta \dot{A}(0) \rangle_0 + \frac{1}{k_B T} \int_0^t dt' \, \langle \delta \dot{\mathcal{N}}(t') \, \delta \dot{A}(0) \rangle_0$$

$$= \frac{1}{k_B T} \int_0^t dt' \, \left\langle \left(\sum_i \dot{H}[x_i(t')] \right) \left(\sum_j \dot{x}_j(0) \, F_{\text{ext}} \right) \right\rangle_0$$

$$= \frac{1}{k_B T} \int_0^t dt' \, \left\langle \left(\sum_i \delta(x_i - x) \, \dot{x}_i(t') \right) \left(\sum_j \dot{x}_j(0) \, F_{\text{ext}} \right) \right\rangle_0$$

$$= \frac{F_{\text{ext}}}{k_B T} \sum_{ij} \int_0^t dt' \, \langle \delta(x_i - x) \, \dot{x}_i(t') \, \dot{x}_j(0) \rangle_0 \qquad (6.20)$$

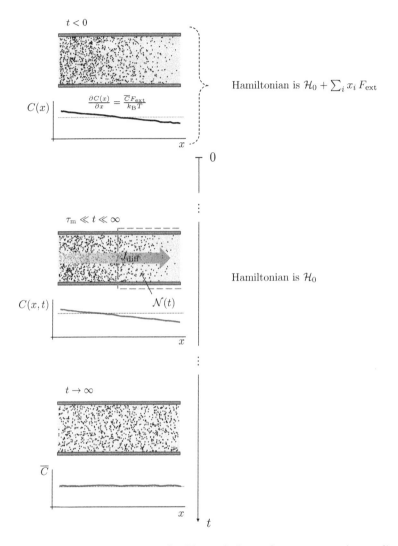

Fig. 6.1 Nonequilibrium relaxation of a dilute solution under a concentration gradient. Only the solute particles are shown in the pictorial representations. The Hamiltonian of the unperturbed reference system yielding a uniform concentration $\overline{C}$ is $\mathcal{H}_0$. (Top) For $t < 0$, a perturbation is introduced to establish a concentration gradient according to Eq. (6.17). This represents an equilibrium situation governed by the Hamiltonian $\mathcal{H}_0 + \sum_i x_i F_{\text{ext}}$. At $t = 0$, the perturbation is suddenly removed and the system evolves dynamically according to the reference Hamiltonian $\mathcal{H}_0$. (Bottom) After an extremely long time, the system returns to an equilibrium situation governed by the reference Hamiltonian $\mathcal{H}_0$ yielding the uniform concentration $\overline{C}$. (Middle) For all times $t \geq 0$, we can monitor the instantaneous number of solute particles $\mathcal{N}(t)$ as defined in Eq. (6.18). The steady-state diffusion flux J_{diff} is valid for a time t that is much larger than τ_{m}, but still much smaller than the time needed to return to a uniform concentration $\overline{C}$.

following from Eq. (6.4). The term $\langle \delta \mathcal{N} \, \delta \dot{A} \rangle_0$ is zero because the velocities and positions are uncorrelated in a simple equilibrium average. The time-correlation function can be further simplified because the reference equilibrium system is expected to be independent of the position x. This implies that the time-correlation function should not depend on the location within the system. This implies that the spatial constraint can be decoupled from the time-correlation function,

$$\langle \delta(x_i - x) \, \dot{x}_i(t) \, \dot{x}_j(0) \rangle_0 = \langle \delta(x_i - x) \rangle_0 \, \langle \dot{x}_i(t) \, \dot{x}_j(0) \rangle_0 \qquad (6.21)$$

The quantity $\langle \delta(x_i - x) \rangle_0$ can be described by simply noting that,

$$\langle \delta(x_i - x) \rangle_0 = \frac{S(x)}{\int dx \, S(x)}$$

$$= \frac{S(x)}{V} \qquad (6.22)$$

where V is the volume of the system and $S(x)$ is the y, z cross-sectional area of the system at x. Furthermore, it is reasonable to assume that, in a dilute solution, the velocity of different solute particles i and j are completely uncorrelated,

$$\langle \dot{x}_i(t) \, \dot{x}_j(0) \rangle_0 = \delta_{ij} \, \langle \dot{x}_1(t) \, \dot{x}_1(0) \rangle_0 \qquad (6.23)$$

where we have arbitrarily chosen solute #1 (all the identical solute particles are equivalent). With these considerations, we have,

$$\frac{d}{dt} \langle \mathcal{N}(t) \rangle = \frac{F_{\text{ext}}}{k_B T} \sum_{ij} \delta_{ij} \frac{S(x)}{V} \int_0^t dt' \, \langle \dot{x}_1(t') \, \dot{x}_1(0) \rangle_0$$

$$= \frac{F_{\text{ext}}}{k_B T} \overline{C} \, S(x) \int_0^t dt' \, \langle \dot{x}_1(t') \, \dot{x}_1(0) \rangle_0 \qquad (6.24)$$

where $\overline{C} = N/V$ is the solute concentration in the uniform reference system. The quasi steady-state diffusion flux is then,

$$J_{\text{diff}} = \lim_{t \gg \tau_m} \frac{1}{S(x)} \frac{d}{dt} \langle \mathcal{N}(t) \rangle$$

$$= \frac{1}{S(x)} \frac{F_{\text{ext}}}{k_B T} \overline{C} \, S(x) \, D$$

$$= -\left(\frac{1}{C} \frac{\partial C(x)}{\partial x} \right) \overline{C} \, D$$

$$= -D \frac{\partial C(x)}{\partial x} \qquad (6.25)$$

where

$$D = \int_0^\infty dt' \, \langle \dot{x}_1(t') \, \dot{x}_1(0) \rangle_0 \tag{6.26}$$

is the coefficient of self-diffusion, here defined in terms of the velocity-velocity time-correlation function of a solute particle 1. We have replaced the limit of τ_m by ∞, which is reasonable because the velocity-velocity time-correlation function is expected to decay to zero within the molecular timescale. The relationship between the diffusive flux and the concentration gradient given by Eq. (6.25) is Fick's law (see also Section 7.1 in Chapter 7).

6.3   Time-correlation function of stationary processes

In general, we will need to consider time-correlation functions of the general form,

$$C_{fg}(t) = \langle f(t')g(t' + t) \rangle \tag{6.27}$$

where $f(t)$ and $g(t)$ are two functions of time with stationary properties (i.e., t' does not affect the result). In practice, $C_{fg}(t)$ can be calculated as a time-average from a trajectory, assuming that it is sufficiently long to sample all the possible states of the system in a manner that is consistent with thermodynamic equilibrium.

$$C_{fg}(t) = \frac{1}{2\mathcal{T}} \int_{-\mathcal{T}}^{\mathcal{T}} f(t')g(t' + t) \, dt' \tag{6.28}$$

or as a direct sum over discrete time-step,

$$C_{fg}(n\Delta t) = \frac{1}{M - n} \sum_{m=1}^{M-n} f(m\Delta t) \, g(m\Delta t + n\Delta t) \tag{6.29}$$

which has to be evaluated for all values of n from 0 to some maximum N. As this requires essentially $N \times M$ operations, the direct sum can become computationally prohibitive if both N and M are large. In this case, a Fourier transform method, described next, is more practical. Introducing the Fourier transform of the correlation function,

$$\widetilde{C}_{fg}(\omega) = \int_{-\infty}^{\infty} C_{fg}(t) \, e^{-i\omega t} dt \tag{6.30}$$

$$= \lim_{T \to \infty} \frac{1}{2T} \int_{-\infty}^{\infty} e^{-i\omega t} \int_{-T}^{T} f(t') \, g(t + t') \, dt' dt$$

$$= \lim_{T \to \infty} \frac{1}{2T} \underbrace{\int_{-T}^{T} f(t') \, e^{i\omega t'} \, dt'}_{\widetilde{f}_T(-\omega)} \underbrace{\int_{-\infty}^{\infty} g(t + t') \, e^{-i\omega(t+t')} dt}_{\widetilde{g}(\omega)}$$

$$= \lim_{T \to \infty} \frac{1}{2T} \, \widetilde{f}_T(-\omega) \, \widetilde{g}(\omega) \tag{6.31}$$

This relation is called the Wiener–Khinchin theorem. The function $\widetilde{C}_{ff}(\omega)$ is generally referred to as the power spectrum of the random signal $f(t)$. The correlation function can then be calculated by the inverse Fourier transform,

$$C_{fg}(t) = \frac{1}{2\pi} \int_{-\infty}^{\infty} d\omega \, e^{i\omega t} \, \widetilde{C}_{fg}(\omega) \tag{6.32}$$

When $f = g$, $C_{ff}(t)$ is called a time autocorrelation function, and the Wiener–Khinchin theorem takes the form:

$$\widetilde{C}_{ff}(\omega) = \lim_{T \to \infty} \frac{1}{2T} \left\| \widetilde{f}(\omega) \right\|^2 \tag{6.33}$$

A number of useful relations can also be derived about time autocorrelation functions in the special case of stationary processes. In particular,

$$\langle f(0)f(t) \rangle = \langle f(-t)f(0) \rangle \tag{6.34}$$

which implies that the autocorrelation function of a stationary signal is an even function, $C(t) = C(-t)$. Furthermore, because

$$\langle \dot{f}(t)f(0) \rangle = -\langle f(0)\dot{f}(-t) \rangle \tag{6.35}$$

we have, in the special case of $t = 0$ that:

$$\langle \dot{f}(0)f(0) \rangle = -\langle f(0)\dot{f}(0) \rangle = 0 \tag{6.36}$$

This can also be seen as a consequence of the fact that the autocorrelation function $C(t)$ is an even function (its derivative must be 0 at $t = 0$). Furthermore, because $C_{ff}(t)$ is an even function of time, the Fourier transform:

$$\tilde{C}_{ff}(\omega) = \lim_{\mathcal{T} \to \infty} \frac{1}{2\mathcal{T}} \left\| \tilde{f}(\omega) \right\|^2 \tag{6.37}$$

can also be written as,

$$\tilde{C}_{ff}(\omega) = \int_{-\infty}^{\infty} C_{ff}(t) \, \cos(\omega t) \, dt$$

$$= 2 \int_{0}^{\infty} C_{ff}(t) \, \cos(\omega t) \, dt \tag{6.38}$$

(the integral with the $\sin(\omega t)$ cancels out). This implies that, in this case, $\tilde{C}_{ff}(\omega)$ is a real and even function of ω. It follows that the time-correlation function is,

$$C_{ff}(t) = \frac{1}{2\pi} \int_{-\infty}^{\infty} \tilde{C}_{ff}(\omega) \, \cos(\omega t) \, d\omega$$

$$= \frac{2}{2\pi} \int_{0}^{\infty} \tilde{C}_{ff}(\omega) \, \cos(\omega t) \, d\omega \tag{6.39}$$

Added note: Fourier and Laplace transforms

The Fourier and inverse Fourier transforms are defined as,

$$\tilde{C}^{(\mathcal{F})}(\omega) = \int_{-\infty}^{\infty} C(t) \, e^{-i\omega t} dt \tag{6.40}$$

and

$$C(t) = \frac{1}{2\pi} \int_{-\infty}^{\infty} \tilde{C}^{(\mathcal{F})}(\omega) \, e^{i\omega t} d\omega \tag{6.41}$$

The Laplace–Fourier transform is defined as,

$$\tilde{C}^{(\mathcal{LF})}(\omega) = \int_{0}^{\infty} C(t) \, e^{-i\omega t} dt \tag{6.42}$$

If the function $C(t)$ is zero for $t < 0$, then $\tilde{C}^{(\mathcal{F})} = \tilde{C}^{(\mathcal{LF})}$ by default. The standard Laplace transform is recovered when $i\omega$ is substituted by the real variable s,

$$\tilde{C}^{(\mathcal{L})}(s) = \int_{0}^{\infty} C(t) \, e^{-st} dt \tag{6.43}$$

If the function $C(t)$ is real and even in t, then the above is

$$\tilde{C}^{(\mathcal{F})}(\omega) = \int_{-\infty}^{\infty} C(t)\, e^{-i\omega t} dt$$

$$= 2\mathscr{R}\left\{ \int_{0}^{\infty} C(t)\, e^{-i\omega t} dt \right\}$$

$$= 2\mathscr{R}\left\{ \tilde{C}^{(\mathcal{LF})}(\omega) \right\} \tag{6.44}$$

The Fourier transform of the time derivative of a function is,

$$\int_{-\infty}^{\infty} \frac{dC(t)}{dt}\, e^{-i\omega t} dt = \int_{-\infty}^{\infty} \frac{d}{dt}\left(C(t)\, e^{-i\omega t} \right) dt + i\omega \int_{-\infty}^{\infty} C(t)\, e^{-i\omega t}\, dt$$

$$= i\omega \tilde{C}^{(\mathcal{F})}(\omega) \tag{6.45}$$

The Laplace–Fourier transform of the time derivative of a function is,

$$\int_{0}^{\infty} \frac{dC(t)}{dt}\, e^{-i\omega t} dt = \int_{0}^{\infty} \frac{d}{dt}\left(C(t)\, e^{-i\omega t} \right) dt + i\omega \int_{0}^{\infty} C(t)\, e^{-i\omega t}\, dt$$

$$= -C(0) + i\omega \tilde{C}^{(\mathcal{LF})}(\omega) \tag{6.46}$$

Similarly, the Laplace transform of the time derivative of a function is,

$$\int_{0}^{\infty} \frac{dC(t)}{dt}\, e^{-st} dt = \int_{0}^{\infty} \frac{d}{dt}\left(C(t)\, e^{-st} \right) dt + s \int_{0}^{\infty} C(t)\, e^{-st}\, dt$$

$$= -C(0) + s\tilde{C}^{(\mathcal{L})}(s) \tag{6.47}$$

Defining a time convolution as,

$$C(t) = \int_{-\infty}^{\infty} G(t')H(t - t')\, dt' \tag{6.48}$$

its Fourier transform is,

$$\tilde{C}^{(\mathcal{F})}(\omega) = \int_{-\infty}^{\infty} C(t)\, e^{-i\omega t} dt$$

$$= \int_{-\infty}^{\infty} \int_{-\infty}^{\infty} G(t')\, H(t - t')\, dt'\, e^{-i\omega t} dt$$

$$= \int_{-\infty}^{\infty} G(t')\, e^{-i\omega t'}\, dt' \int_{-\infty}^{\infty} H(t - t')\, e^{-i\omega(t - t')} dt$$

$$= \tilde{G}^{(\mathcal{F})}(\omega)\, \tilde{H}^{(\mathcal{F})}(\omega) \tag{6.49}$$

If the function $G(t)$ and $H(t)$ are equal to zero when $t < 0$ (or $t > 0$) then their Fourier transforms become Laplace–Fourier transforms. The convolution relation also applies to the Laplace transform.

6.4   Green–Kubo linear response theory

We have described in Section 6.1 the response of a system prepared in a nonequilibrium state by a small perturbation, which is then turned off at $t = 0$. All the expressions involve time-correlation functions in the reference system $\mathcal{H}_0$. This simple and very specific situation made it possible to derive many key expressions with relatively little effort. More generally, one could consider a system with Hamiltonian $\mathcal{H} = \mathcal{H}_0 - AF(t)$, where $\mathcal{H}_0$ is the Hamiltonian of a reference system, and $-AF(t)$ is a time-dependent perturbation that is turned on after $t = 0$. We shall see that the average of an observable B in response to the perturbation has the form:

$$\langle B(t) \rangle = \langle B \rangle_0 + \frac{1}{k_{\mathrm{B}} T} \int_0^t dt' \, \langle B(t - t') \dot{A}(0) \rangle_0 \, F(t') \qquad (6.50)$$

Eq. (6.50) is a principal result of Green–Kubo theory of linear response [Green (1952, 1954); Kubo (1957)]. As with the previous treatment leading to Eq. (6.4), the central aspect of the nonequilibrium response to small perturbation is represented by time-correlation functions measured in the unperturbed system $\mathcal{H}_0$.

The similarity with Eq. (6.4) is further apparent if $F(t)$ is a step-function, such that the perturbation A is suddenly turned on at $t = 0$. To derive this expression, however, a more elaborate formalism is required than what was used in Section 6.1. This includes the representation of the Hamiltonian dynamics of the nonequilibrium probability distribution in phase space. In the Hamiltonian formulation of classical dynamics,

$$\mathcal{H} = \sum_i \frac{p_i^2}{2M_i} + U(\ldots, x_i, \ldots) \qquad (6.51)$$

where p_i and x_i are the momentum and coordinate associated with the i-th degree of freedom, respectively (we are assuming cartesian coordinates for the sake of simplicity). The dynamical equations of motions are,

$$\dot{x}_i = \frac{\partial \mathcal{H}}{\partial p_i} \qquad (6.52)$$

and

$$\dot{p}_i = -\frac{\partial \mathcal{H}}{\partial x_i} \qquad (6.53)$$

It is possible to express the time evolution of a dynamical variable A in terms of a Taylor series:

$$A(t) = A(0) + \dot{A}(0)t + \frac{1}{2!}\ddot{A}(0)t^2 + \cdots \tag{6.54}$$

where the time derivative of A is

$$\dot{A} = \sum_i \frac{\partial A}{\partial x_i}\dot{x}_i + \frac{\partial A}{\partial p_i}\dot{p}_i$$

$$= \sum_i \frac{\partial A}{\partial x_i}\frac{\partial \mathcal{H}}{\partial p_i} - \frac{\partial A}{\partial p_i}\frac{\partial \mathcal{H}}{\partial x_i}$$

$$= -\{\mathcal{H}, A\} \tag{6.55}$$

where the differential operator,

$$\frac{\partial \cdots}{\partial t} = \{\mathcal{H}, \cdots\}$$

$$= \sum_i \frac{\partial \mathcal{H}}{\partial x_i}\frac{\partial \cdots}{\partial p_i} - \frac{\partial \mathcal{H}}{\partial p_i}\frac{\partial \cdots}{\partial x_i} \tag{6.56}$$

is called a Poisson bracket, an important concept of classical dynamics. It follows that we can formally write the Taylor expansion as,

$$A(t) = e^{-\{\mathcal{H}, \cdots\}t}A \tag{6.57}$$

It is also of interest to monitor the evolution of the time-dependent density of dynamical systems in phase space, $P(\mathbf{x}, \mathbf{p}, t)$. As a result of dynamical propagation, $P(\mathbf{x}, \mathbf{p}, t)$ must be conserved. Furthermore, the evolution of the system from the point in phase space $(\mathbf{x}, \mathbf{p})$ is completely deterministic and depends only on initial conditions. Considering the propagation from $(\mathbf{x} - \Delta\mathbf{x}, \mathbf{p} - \Delta\mathbf{p})$ to $(\mathbf{x}, \mathbf{p})$ during a time-step Δt, we have:

$$P(\mathbf{x}, \mathbf{p}, t + \Delta t) = P(\mathbf{x} - \Delta\mathbf{x}, \mathbf{p} - \Delta\mathbf{p}, t) \tag{6.58}$$

We then shift the $\mathbf{x}$ position by $+\Delta\mathbf{x}$:

$$P(\mathbf{x} + \Delta\mathbf{x}, \mathbf{p}, t + \Delta t) = P(\mathbf{x}, \mathbf{p} - \Delta\mathbf{p}, t) \tag{6.59}$$

and carry out a Taylor expansion for small Δt around the point $(\mathbf{x}, \mathbf{p}, t)$ on both sides of the equation,

$$P + \sum_i \frac{\partial P}{\partial x_i}\frac{p_i}{m_i}\Delta t + \frac{\partial P}{\partial t}\Delta t + \cdots = P - \sum_i \frac{\partial P}{\partial p_i}F_i\Delta t + \cdots \tag{6.60}$$

where $\Delta x_i = (p_i/m_i)\Delta t$ and $\Delta p_i = F_i(\mathbf{x} - \Delta \mathbf{x})\Delta t$ have been used. Keeping only the first-order terms in Δt we get,

$$\frac{\partial P}{\partial t} = -\sum_i \frac{\partial P}{\partial x_i}\frac{p_i}{m_i} + \frac{\partial P}{\partial p_i}F_i$$

$$\frac{\partial P}{\partial t} = -\sum_i \frac{\partial P}{\partial x_i}\frac{p_i}{m} + \frac{\partial P}{\partial p_i}F_i$$

$$\frac{\partial P}{\partial t} = \sum_i \frac{\partial \mathcal{H}}{\partial x_i}\frac{\partial P}{\partial p_i} - \frac{\partial \mathcal{H}}{\partial p_i}\frac{\partial P}{\partial x_i}$$

$$\frac{\partial P}{\partial t} = \{\mathcal{H}, P\} \tag{6.61}$$

The time propagation of P, therefore, will be,

$$P(t) = e^{\{\mathcal{H},\dots\}t}P \tag{6.62}$$

(Notice the sign difference with respect to the propagation of the dynamical variable A above.) An alternative derivation proceeds directly from the continuity equation in phase space. Let $\mathbf{\Gamma} = (\mathbf{\Gamma}_1, \mathbf{\Gamma}_2) \equiv (\mathbf{x}, \mathbf{p})$ represent a point in phase space. The probability density to find the system at the point $\mathbf{\Gamma}$ at time t is $P(\mathbf{\Gamma}, t)$. From conservation of the probability density, we can write,

$$\frac{\partial P}{\partial t} + \mathbf{\nabla}_\mathbf{\Gamma} \cdot \mathbf{J} = 0 \tag{6.63}$$

where $\mathbf{\nabla}\cdot$ represents the divergence of the flux $\mathbf{J}$ at the point $\mathbf{\Gamma}$ in phase space. The local flux at the point $\mathbf{\Gamma}$ in phase space is simply $\mathbf{J} = \dot{\mathbf{\Gamma}}P = (\dot{\mathbf{\Gamma}}_1, \dot{\mathbf{\Gamma}}_2)P$, where $\dot{\mathbf{\Gamma}}$ represents the rate of change of this point in phase space along a dynamical trajectory. By definition, we have $(\dot{\mathbf{\Gamma}}_1, \dot{\mathbf{\Gamma}}_2) \equiv (\dot{\mathbf{x}}, \dot{\mathbf{p}})$ and $(\dot{x}_i, \dot{p}_i) = (p_i/m_i, F_i) = (\partial \mathcal{H}/\partial p_i, -\partial \mathcal{H}/\partial x_i)$ from Hamilton's equations of motion. Thus,

$$\frac{\partial P}{\partial t} + \mathbf{\nabla}_{\mathbf{\Gamma}_1} \cdot (\dot{\mathbf{\Gamma}}_1 P) + \mathbf{\nabla}_{\mathbf{\Gamma}_2} \cdot (\dot{\mathbf{\Gamma}}_2 P) = 0$$

$$\frac{\partial P}{\partial t} + \sum_i \frac{\partial}{\partial x_i}\left(\frac{p_i}{m_i}P\right) + \frac{\partial}{\partial p_i}(F_i P) = 0$$

$$\frac{\partial P}{\partial t} + \sum_i \frac{p_i}{m_i}\frac{\partial P}{\partial x_i} + F_i\frac{\partial P}{\partial p_i} = 0$$

$$\frac{\partial P}{\partial t} - \{\mathcal{H}, P\} = 0 \tag{6.64}$$

Let us now consider a system with Hamiltonian $\mathcal{H} = \mathcal{H}_0 - AF(t)$, where $\mathcal{H}_0$ is the Hamiltonian of a reference system, and $-AF(t)$ is a time-dependent perturbation. The equilibrium distribution of the unperturbed system is $P_0 = Q_0^{-1} e^{-\mathcal{H}_0/k_B T}$, .where Q_0 is the partition function,

$$Q_0 = \int d\mathbf{\Gamma} \, e^{-\mathcal{H}_0(\mathbf{\Gamma})/k_B T} \tag{6.65}$$

and

$$\frac{\partial P_0}{\partial t} = \{\mathcal{H}_0, P_0\}$$

$$= \left\{\mathcal{H}_0, Q_0^{-1} e^{-\mathcal{H}_0/k_B T}\right\}$$

$$= 0 \tag{6.66}$$

because $\{\mathcal{H}_0, \mathcal{H}_0\} = 0$. Here, we are mainly interested in the deviations from the equilibrium reference system. To describe the further development of the system, we examine the time evolution of the probability density in phase space written as $P_0 + \Delta P$,

$$\frac{\partial P}{\partial t} = \{\mathcal{H}, P\}$$

$$\frac{\partial(P_0 + \Delta P)}{\partial t} = \{\mathcal{H}_0 - AF(t), P\}$$

$$\frac{\partial P_0}{\partial t} + \frac{\partial \Delta P}{\partial t} = \{\mathcal{H}_0, P_0 + \Delta P\} - \{A, P\} F(t)$$

$$\frac{\partial P_0}{\partial t} + \frac{\partial \Delta P}{\partial t} = \{\mathcal{H}_0, P_0\} + \{\mathcal{H}_0, \Delta P\} - \{A, P\} F(t)$$

$$\frac{\partial \Delta P}{\partial t} = \{\mathcal{H}_0, \Delta P\} - \{A, P\} F(t)$$

$$\frac{\partial \Delta P}{\partial t} - \{\mathcal{H}_0, \Delta P\} = -\{A, P\} F(t)$$

$$e^{\{\mathcal{H}_0, \dots\} t} \frac{d}{dt} \left(e^{-\{\mathcal{H}_0, \dots\} t} \Delta P\right) = -\{A, P\} F(t)$$

$$\frac{d}{dt} \left(e^{-\{\mathcal{H}_0, \dots\} t} \Delta P(t)\right) = -e^{-\{\mathcal{H}_0, \dots\} t} \{A, P\} F(t)$$

$$e^{-\{\mathcal{H}_0, \dots\} t} \Delta P(t) = -\int_0^t dt' \, e^{-\{\mathcal{H}_0, \dots\} t'} \{A, P\} F(t')$$

$$\Delta P(t) = -\int_0^t dt' \, e^{-\{\mathcal{H}_0, \dots\}(t'-t)} \{A, P\} F(t') \tag{6.67}$$

We now assume that the perturbation is small and that we can substitute P by P_0 in the integral on the r.h.s.,

$$\Delta P(t) = - \int_0^t dt'\, e^{-\{\mathcal{H}_0,\dots\}(t'-t)} \{A, P_0\}\, F(t')$$

$$= \frac{1}{k_B T} \int_0^t dt'\, e^{-\{\mathcal{H}_0,\dots\}(t'-t)} \dot{A}\, P_0\, F(t') \qquad (6.68)$$

where

$$\{A, P_0\} = \left\{ A, Q_0^{-1} e^{-\mathcal{H}_0/k_B T} \right\}$$

$$= -\frac{1}{k_B T} \{A, \mathcal{H}_0\}\, Q_0^{-1} e^{-\mathcal{H}_0/k_B T}$$

$$= -\frac{1}{k_B T} \dot{A}\, P_0 \qquad (6.69)$$

has been used. Integrating over phase space $\mathbf{\Gamma}$, the average of a dynamical variable B in the perturbed ensemble relative to the reference ensemble P_0 is

$$\langle \Delta B(t) \rangle = \langle B(t) \rangle - \langle B \rangle_0$$

$$= \int d\mathbf{\Gamma}\, B\, \Delta P(t)$$

$$= \frac{1}{k_B T} \int d\mathbf{\Gamma} \int_0^t dt'\, B \left[e^{-\{\mathcal{H}_0,\dots\}(t'-t)} \dot{A}\, P_0(\mathbf{\Gamma}) \right] F(t')$$

$$= \frac{1}{k_B T} \int d\mathbf{\Gamma} \int_0^t dt' \left[e^{-\{\mathcal{H}_0,\dots\}(t-t')} B \right] \dot{A}\, P_0(\mathbf{\Gamma})\, F(t')$$

$$= \frac{1}{k_B T} \int d\mathbf{\Gamma} \int_0^t dt'\, B(t-t')\, \dot{A}\, P_0(\mathbf{\Gamma})\, F(t')$$

$$= \frac{1}{k_B T} \int_0^t dt' \int d\mathbf{\Gamma}\, B(t-t')\, \dot{A}\, P_0(\mathbf{\Gamma})\, F(t')$$

$$= \frac{1}{k_B T} \int_0^t dt'\, \langle B(t-t')\dot{A}(0) \rangle_0\, F(t') \qquad (6.70)$$

which is Eq. (6.50) stated previously. In the following, we will examine a few examples to illustrate the application of linear response.

6.5 Particle subjected to an external force

Let us consider a system with a time-dependent external force F_{ext} applied to a particle in the x-direction. The perturbed Hamiltonian is $\mathcal{H}_0 - xF_{ext}(t)$. We are interested in the average velocity of the particle under the influence of the external force. Thus, in Eq. (6.50), $A = x$ and $B(t) = v_x(t)$. Accordingly, the average velocity is

$$\langle v(t) \rangle = \frac{1}{k_B T} \int_0^t dt' \, \langle v_x(t - t') v_x(0) \rangle_0 \, F_{ext}(t') \tag{6.71}$$

The frequency-dependent mobility of the particle can be displayed by taking the Laplace–Fourier transform on both sides of the equation, yielding,

$$\langle \widetilde{v}(\omega) \rangle = \widetilde{\mu}(\omega) \widetilde{F}_{ext}(\omega) \tag{6.72}$$

where the frequency-dependent mobility $\widetilde{\mu}(\omega)$ is,

$$\widetilde{\mu}(\omega) = \frac{1}{k_B T} \, \widetilde{C}_v(\omega)$$

$$= \frac{1}{k_B T} \int_0^\infty C_v(t) \, e^{-i\omega t} \, dt \tag{6.73}$$

with

$$\langle \widetilde{v}(\omega) \rangle = \int_0^\infty \langle v(t) \rangle \, e^{-i\omega t} \, dt \tag{6.74}$$

and

$$\widetilde{F}_{ext}(\omega) = \int_0^\infty F_{ext}(t) \, e^{-i\omega t} \, dt \tag{6.75}$$

It should be noted that $\widetilde{C}_v(\omega)$ denotes a Laplace–Fourier transform, reflecting the causality relationship that is implicitly built in the time convolution.

An important special case is when the external force is constant, ultimately leading to a quasi steady-state drift of the particle. The average drift velocity after a very long time is,

$$v_{drift} = \lim_{t \to \infty} \langle v_x(t) \rangle$$

$$= \widetilde{\mu}(0) \, F_{ext}$$

$$= \frac{D}{k_B T} \, F_{ext} \tag{6.76}$$

where D is the self-diffusion coefficient defined in Eq. (6.26). The steady state drift velocity is estabilished when the external force is canceled by an opposing frictional force, $-\gamma v_{\text{drift}}$. Here, we can see that the dissipative friction coefficient γ is related to the spontaneously diffusional fluctuations, $\gamma = k_B T / D$. This relationship between γ and D is called the Einstein relation. This is a manifestation of the "fluctuation-dissipation" theorem. This example may be easily extended to the case of a system representing an electrolyte solution under the influence of a constant external electric field of magnitude E_{ext} in the x-direction that is switched on at time $t = 0$. The perturbed Hamiltonian is

$$\mathcal{H} = \mathcal{H}_0 - \sum_i q_i x_i E_{\text{ext}} \tag{6.77}$$

We would like to calculate the average electric current $I_x = \sum_i q_i v_i$ in the x-direction under the influence of the perturbation,

$$\langle I_x \rangle = \frac{1}{k_B T} \sum_{i,j} q_i q_j D_{ij} E_{\text{ext}} \tag{6.78}$$

where D_{ij} is,

$$D_{ij} = \int_0^\infty dt' \, \langle v_{i,x}(t') v_{j,x}(0) \rangle_0 \tag{6.79}$$

representing the cross-diffusion coefficient.

6.6 Particle undergoing an imposed time-dependent movement

Another interesting example is the case of a particle that is held fixed at x_0 for a long time, and then, is suddenly forced to undergo the displacement $\Delta x(t)$ at time $t = 0$. The Hamiltonian is

$$\mathcal{H} = \mathcal{H}_0 + \frac{\partial \mathcal{H}_0}{\partial x} \Delta x(t)$$
$$= \mathcal{H}_0 - \mathcal{F}_x \Delta x(t) \tag{6.80}$$

where $\mathcal{H}_0$ is the reference state with the particle fixed at x_0, $\Delta x(t) = x(t) - x_0$, and $\mathcal{F}_x$ is the force from the system acting on the particle. Here, $\Delta x(t)$ is a time-dependent function because we are deliberately moving the tagged particle at constant velocity v_x, with $\Delta x(t) = v_x t$. We assume that there is no mean force in the reference system, with $\langle \mathcal{F}_x \rangle_0 = 0$. The observable we are interested in is the total force acting on the particle arising from the interactions with all other particles in the system,

$$\langle \mathcal{F}_x(t) \rangle = \left\langle \frac{\partial \mathcal{H}_0}{\partial x} \right\rangle_0 + \left\langle \frac{\partial^2 \mathcal{H}_0}{\partial x^2} \right\rangle_0 \Delta x(t)$$

$$+ \frac{1}{k_B T} \int_0^t dt' \, \langle \mathcal{F}_x(t-t')\dot{\mathcal{F}}_x(0) \rangle_0 \, \Delta x(t')$$

$$= \langle \mathcal{F}_x \rangle_0 - \frac{1}{k_B T} \langle \mathcal{F}_x \mathcal{F}_x \rangle_0 \, \Delta x(t)$$

$$+ \frac{1}{k_B T} \int_0^t dt' \, \langle \mathcal{F}_x(t-t')\dot{\mathcal{F}}_x(0) \rangle_0 \, \Delta x(t') \qquad (6.81)$$

where we have used the identity $\langle \partial^2 \mathcal{H}_0/\partial x^2 \rangle_0 = -\langle \mathcal{F}_x \mathcal{F}_x \rangle_0 / k_B T$. The remaining terms may be rewritten as,

$$\langle \mathcal{F}_x(t) \rangle = -\frac{1}{k_B T} \langle \mathcal{F}_x \mathcal{F}_x \rangle_0 \, \Delta x(t')$$

$$+ \frac{1}{k_B T} \int_0^t dt' \, \langle \mathcal{F}_x(t-t')\dot{\mathcal{F}}_x(0) \rangle_0 \, \Delta x(t')$$

$$= -\frac{1}{k_B T} \langle \mathcal{F}_x \mathcal{F}_x \rangle_0 \, \Delta x(t)$$

$$- \frac{1}{k_B T} \int_0^t dt' \, \langle \dot{\mathcal{F}}_x(t-t')\mathcal{F}_x(0) \rangle_0 \, \Delta x(t')$$

$$= -\frac{1}{k_B T} \langle \mathcal{F}_x \mathcal{F}_x \rangle_0 \, \Delta x(t)$$

$$+ \frac{1}{k_B T} \int_0^t dt' \left(\frac{d}{dt'} \langle \mathcal{F}_x(t-t')\mathcal{F}_x(0) \rangle_0 \right) \Delta x(t')$$

$$= -\frac{1}{k_B T} \langle \mathcal{F}_x \mathcal{F}_x \rangle_0 \, \Delta x(t)$$

$$+ \frac{1}{k_B T} \int_0^t dt' \left[\frac{d}{dt'} \Big(\langle \mathcal{F}_x(t-t')\mathcal{F}_x(0) \rangle_0 \, \Delta x(t') \Big) \right.$$

$$\left. - \langle \mathcal{F}_x(t-t')\mathcal{F}_x(0) \rangle_0 \, \frac{d\Delta x(t')}{dt'} \right]$$

$$= -\frac{1}{k_\mathrm{B} T} \langle \mathcal{F}_x \mathcal{F}_x \rangle_0 \, \Delta x(t)$$

$$+ \frac{1}{k_\mathrm{B} T} \left[\langle \mathcal{F}_x(t - t') \mathcal{F}_x(0) \rangle_0 \, \Delta x(t') \Big|_0^t \right.$$

$$\left. - \int_0^t dt' \langle \mathcal{F}_x(t - t') \mathcal{F}_x(0) \rangle_0 \, v_x(t') \right]$$

$$= -\frac{1}{k_\mathrm{B} T} \langle \mathcal{F}_x \mathcal{F}_x \rangle_0 \, \Delta x(t)$$

$$+ \frac{1}{k_\mathrm{B} T} \langle \mathcal{F}_x \mathcal{F}_x \rangle_0 \, \Delta x(t) - \frac{1}{k_\mathrm{B} T} \int_0^t dt' \, \langle \mathcal{F}_x(t - t') \mathcal{F}_x(0) \rangle_0 \, v_x(t')$$

$$= -\frac{1}{k_\mathrm{B} T} \int_0^t dt' \, \langle \mathcal{F}_x(t - t') \mathcal{F}_x(0) \rangle_0 \, v_x(t') \tag{6.82}$$

or

$$\lim_{t \to \infty} \langle \mathcal{F}_x(t) \rangle = -\gamma \, v_x \tag{6.83}$$

where γ is the friction coefficient,

$$\gamma = \frac{1}{k_\mathrm{B} T} \int_0^\infty dt' \, \langle \mathcal{F}_x(t') \mathcal{F}_x(0) \rangle_0 \tag{6.84}$$

The friction coefficient is related to the integral of the autocorrelation function of the force acting on the *fixed* tagged particle. This relationship between the friction coefficient γ and the integral of the force-force time-correlation function is called the second fluctuation-dissipation theorem.

Chapter 7

Effective dynamics of reduced models

The most striking drawback of all-atom molecular dynamics (MD) is that the trajectory of a large number of atoms must be calculated, although only a small number among them might be truly relevant to understanding the function that one wishes to investigate. An attractive strategy would be to focus only on the dynamics of the most relevant variables, and yet retain the ability to represent all their microscopic properties (structural and dynamical) correctly. The problem of representing the dynamics of a reduced set of degrees of freedom that is part of a large complex system, is a subject that has been extensively explored in statistical mechanical theories over the last 50 years. At the most rigorous level are the ideas introduced by Zwanzig (1965) and Mori (1965), which consists of "projecting out" uninteresting degrees of freedom, in order to develop an effective but physically correct dynamical scheme representing the time evolution of the most "relevant" degrees of freedom realistically. According to this analysis, the reduced set of coordinates treated explicitly evolves according to an effective nondeterministic dynamics that displays an unpredictable random and stochastic character. In contrast, because it accounts for all the degrees of freedom explicitly, the effective classical MD trajectory of the all-atom system, calculated according to Newton's classical laws of motion, is completely deterministic. The effective dynamics of reduced models provides important conceptual frameworks for representing a wide range of diffusional and relaxation processes in complex molecular systems.

7.1 Random walk and diffusion

Before treating a more complex type of stochastic motion, it is illuminating to first examine the properties of a simple random walk of a single particle in one dimension, where it can reside at equally spaced discrete positions, $\ldots, x - 2\Delta x, x - \Delta x, x, x + \Delta x, x + 2\Delta x, \ldots$ (Figure 7.1). Let us assume that the particle starts its random walk at position x at time $t = 0$. At a fixed time interval Δt, the particle can either make a jump to the right to position $x + \Delta x$, or the left to position $x - \Delta x$. The probability to make a $\pm \Delta x$ jump is p, and the probability to remain at x is $(1 - 2p)$. On average, the displacement of the particle after one jump is,

$$\langle x(\Delta t) - x(0) \rangle = p \times (-\Delta x) + (1 - 2p) \times (0) + p \times (+\Delta x)$$
$$= 0 \tag{7.1}$$

and the mean square deviation after one jump is

$$\langle ||x(\Delta t) - x(0)||^2 \rangle = p \times (-\Delta x)^2 + (1 - 2p) \times (0)^2 + p \times (+\Delta x)^2$$
$$= 2p(\Delta x)^2 \tag{7.2}$$

Because all the jumps are statistically independent, the average displacement of the particle after n jumps is still equal to 0, while the mean square deviation is $n(2p\Delta x^2)$. Expressing this result in terms of the total time of the trajectory $t = n\Delta t$ yields:

$$\langle ||x(\Delta t) - x(0)||^2 \rangle = 2 \left(\frac{p(\Delta x)^2}{\Delta t} \right) t$$
$$= 2Dt \tag{7.3}$$

where $D = p(\Delta x)^2 / \Delta t$ is the diffusion coefficient. D has dimension of length square per time. Thus, the position of a particle undergoing a purely diffusive motion does not shift on average. In that sense, the random walk of the particle is symmetric and unbiased — it is as likely to move in both $\pm \Delta x$-directions. This is visible in Figure 7.2, displaying multiple samples of the random walk $x(t)$, where all the particles started at the same position

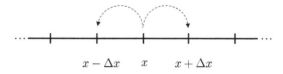

$$x - \Delta x \qquad x \qquad x + \Delta x$$

Fig. 7.1 Schematic random walk of a particle in one dimension.

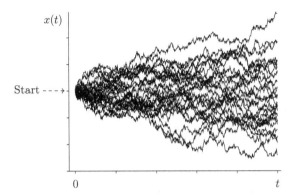

Fig. 7.2 Multiple samples of the random walk of a particle in one dimension as a function of time generated according to the process shown in Figure 7.1. All the particles started at the same x position (indicated by an arrow).

along x. However, an important observation is that the mean square deviation of the particle grows linearly with time. This is in striking contrast with, for example, the trajectory of a particle at constant velocity v, which would yield a mean square deviation growing quadratically with time.

This describes the diffusive motion of a single particle in one dimension. It is worthwhile examining the consequences of this simple random walk mechanism on the net flux through the system when a large number of noninteracting particles are present. The number of particles at each position at time t is $N(x, t)$, and the number of particles per unit length (concentration) at time t is $C(x, t) \equiv N(x, t)/\Delta x$. We assume that the particles independently do not interact with one another, and follow the same random jumps dynamics at a fixed time interval. After one jump, the average number of particles ΔN crossing the boundary between x and $x + \Delta x$ is given by the number of particles jumping toward the right minus the number of particles jumping toward the left,

$$\Delta N = pN(x, t) - pN(x + \Delta x, t) \qquad (7.4)$$

where $N(x)$ and $N(x + \Delta x)$ is the number particles at x and $x + \Delta x$, respectively. The net flux of particle, J_{diff}, the average number of particles crossing the boundary per unit of time is equal to $\Delta N/\Delta t$:

$$
\begin{aligned}
J_{\text{diff}} &= \frac{p}{\Delta t}\left(N(x, t) - N(x + \Delta x, t)\right) \\
&= \frac{p\Delta x}{\Delta t}\left(\frac{N(x, t)}{\Delta x} - \frac{N(x + \Delta x, t)}{\Delta x}\right)
\end{aligned}
$$

$$= \frac{p\Delta x}{\Delta t}\left(C(x,t) - C(x+\Delta x, t)\right)$$

$$= \frac{p(\Delta x)^2}{\Delta t}\left(\frac{C(x,t) - C(x+\Delta x, t)}{\Delta x}\right)$$

$$= -D\left(\frac{C(x+\Delta x) - C(x,t)}{\Delta x}\right) \tag{7.5}$$

In the limit where $\Delta x \to 0$, we get:

$$J_{\text{diff}} = -D\frac{\partial C(x,t)}{\partial x} \tag{7.6}$$

This equation can be recognized as Fick's law (Figure 7.3), which states that there is an average diffusive flux J_{diff} in the direction opposite to a concentration gradient. In Section 6.2 of Chapter 6, we arrived at the same result, Eq. (6.25), by considering the linear response of the system to a perturbation. Here, because we explicitly assumed that there are no interactions between the particles, this analysis makes it clear that the macroscopic diffusive flux in the direction opposite to the concentration gradient arises spontaneously from the unbiased random walk of independent particles. From the conservation of the total concentration, we can write,

$$\frac{\partial C}{\partial t} + \frac{\partial J_{\text{diff}}}{\partial x} = 0 \tag{7.7}$$

(In three dimensions, this equation would be written as $\partial C/\partial t + \boldsymbol{\nabla}\cdot\mathbf{J}_{\text{diff}} = 0$.) Combining Fick's law with the conservation relation yields the classical diffusion equation,

$$\frac{\partial C}{\partial t} = D\frac{\partial^2 C}{\partial x^2} \tag{7.8}$$

It is easy to verify that,

$$C(x,t) = \frac{1}{\sqrt{4\pi Dt}}\, e^{-(x-x_0)^2/4Dt} \tag{7.9}$$

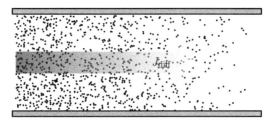

Fig. 7.3 Illustration of Fick's law stating that there is a net diffusive flux of particle J in the direction opposite to a concentration gradient. See also Figure 6.1 in Chapter 6.

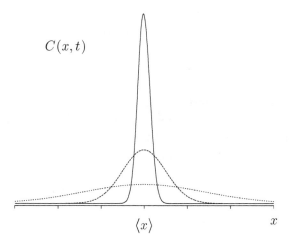

Fig. 7.4 Diffusive spread of a substance in space. There is no net displacement and the mean square deviation increases linearly with time.

is a solution to the diffusion equation when the concentration is sharply focused at x_0 at $t = 0$. This allows us to calculate the mean position,

$$\langle x(t)\rangle = \int dx\, x(t)\, C(x,t)$$

$$= x_0 \qquad\qquad (7.10)$$

and the mean square displacement explicitly as a function of time,

$$\langle ||x(t) - x_0||^2\rangle = \int dx\, (x(t) - x_0)^2\, C(x,t)$$

$$= 2Dt \qquad\qquad (7.11)$$

Thus, the characteristic of a diffusion process, underlined implicitly by Fick's law, is that there is no net displacement ($\langle x\rangle$ is a constant), while the mean square displacement increases linearly with time as $2Dt$. This situation is illustrated in Figure 7.4. In contrast, the ballistic motion of a particle keeping a constant velocity in vacuum would yield a mean square displacement with a quadratic dependence on time, $(x(t) - x_0)^2 = (v_0 t)^2$.

7.2 Friction and damped motion

Having explored the consequences of discrete random jump dynamics, and how it leads to the diffusion equation, we return to a slightly more realistic situation in which the motion of the particle takes place continuously in space and time. Let us examine the motion of a particle immersed in a liquid. We monitor its average displacement in response to an applied external force F_{ext}. Typically, we expect that the particle will reach a maximum drift velocity that is proportional to the magnitude of the force. The rational is that the frictional drag from the liquid gives rise to an effective force opposing the motion of the particle, $F_{\text{drag}} = -\gamma v$, where γ is the friction coefficient. The maximum velocity is reached when the frictional drag is equal and opposite to the external force, $F_{\text{drag}} = -F_{\text{ext}}$, thus $v_{\text{drift}} = F_{\text{ext}}/\gamma$ (see Section 6.5 in Chapter 6). The frictional drag incorporates the average effect of the surrounding liquid on the tagged particle. If there was a concentration $[C]$ of independent particles experiencing the same external force, then a macroscopic flux $J_{\text{drift}} = v_{\text{drift}}[C]$ would be produced. This example highlights the fact that γ is a transport coefficient (the mobility of the particle).

Let us now consider the dynamical movement of the tagged particle again, but in the absence of this external force. The classical equation of motion is,

$$m\frac{dv}{dt} = -\gamma v \tag{7.12}$$

Assuming that the initial velocity is $v(0)$, the solution of the equation is

$$v(t) = v(0)e^{-\gamma t/m} \tag{7.13}$$

The quantity $\tau = m/\gamma$ has the dimension of a relaxation time. As illustrated in Figure 7.5, the velocity decays to 0 after a long time due to the

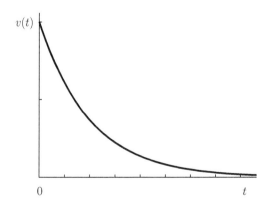

Fig. 7.5 Relaxation of the velocity of a particle subjected to a frictional drag. After a long time, the velocity decays to 0.

frictional drag. According to this simple treatment, the average velocity of the tagged particle will decay to 0 within a relaxing time of τ.

7.3 Langevin equation

If the liquid and the tagged particle are in thermodynamic equilibrium then the velocity of the particle should not relax to a unique value but, rather, must be statistically consistent with the Maxwell distribution. This suggests that Eq. (7.12) above is incomplete; the total force acting on the particle should include some other contribution in addition to the frictional drag $-\gamma v$. Indeed, the latter represents the systematic effect of dissipation due to the surrounding liquid. But the tagged particle should be kicked and accelerated by rapid and frequent collisions from the surrounding particles. This must be taken into account to realistically mimic the dynamics of a particle in thermodynamic equilibrium. To this end, we introduce a time-dependent force $f(t)$ randomly kicking the tagged particle:

$$m\frac{dv}{dt} = -\gamma v + f(t) \tag{7.14}$$

Eq. (7.14) is called the Langevin equation. The time-dependent force $f(t)$ of the Langevin equation is meant to represent the random impulses arising from the surrounding solvent (Figure 7.6). Typically, the amplitude of the random force $f(t)$ is assumed to have a Gaussian character with $\langle f(t) \rangle = 0$ on average. It is also assumed that force varies very rapidly and in an uncorrelated manner. In practice, this means that the value of the random force at a given time t is statistically independent to the value of the force at some other time t'. Mathematically, this implies that the

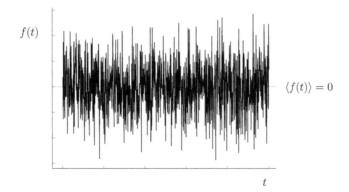

Fig. 7.6 Rapidly varying uncorrelated random noise.

force autocorrelation function $\langle f(t)f(0)\rangle$ is a sharply peaked function close to ≈ 0.

The random force is kicking the particle, giving it energy, while the friction is dissipating the motion of the particle. If the random force was too weak relative to the friction, the particle would effectively have very little velocity. Conversely, if the random force was providing too much power relative to the friction, the particle would effectively have too much velocity. At equilibrium, we know that the mean square deviation of the velocity $\langle v^2 \rangle$ should be equal to $k_B T/m$ according to the equipartition theorem. Therefore, in order to have a physically correct Langevin equation that is consistent with the proper equilibrium behavior, there must be an appropriate balance between the amount of power provided by the random force and the amount of dissipative friction acting on the particle. To examine this question, let us rewrite the formal solution to the stochastic differential equation with the aid of the integrating factor $e^{-\gamma t/m}$,

$$\frac{dv}{dt} = -\frac{\gamma}{m}v + \frac{f(t)}{m}$$

$$e^{-\gamma t/m}\frac{d}{dt}\left(v(t)\,e^{\gamma t/m}\right) = \frac{f(t)}{m}$$

$$\int_0^t d\left(v(t')e^{\gamma t'/m}\right) = \int_0^t dt'\ e^{\gamma t'/m}\,\frac{f(t')}{m}$$

$$v(t)e^{\gamma t/m}\Big|_0^t = \int_0^t dt'\ e^{\gamma t'/m}\,\frac{f(t')}{m}$$

$$v(t) = e^{-\gamma t/m}\left[v(0) + \frac{1}{m}\int_0^t dt'\ e^{\gamma t'/m}\,f(t')\right] \quad (7.15)$$

This closed-form solution allows us to express the average velocity as,

$$\langle v(t)\rangle = v(0)e^{-\gamma t/m} \quad (7.16)$$

which displays the exponential relaxation that we already obtained. Similarly, we can express the square of the velocity as,

$$\langle v^2(t)\rangle = e^{-2\gamma t/m}\left[v^2(0) + \underbrace{\frac{1}{m^2}\int_0^t dt'\int_0^t dt''\ e^{\gamma(t'+t'')/m}\,\langle f(t')f(t'')\rangle}_{\text{need to express this term}}\right]$$

$$(7.17)$$

We have to express the double integral over t' and t'' in Eq. (7.17). Because $\langle f(t')f(t'')\rangle$ is a sharply peaked function, $t' \approx t''$, and the double integral can be expressed as,

$$\int_0^t dt' \int_0^t dt'' e^{\gamma(t'+t'')/m} \langle f(t')f(t'')\rangle = \int_0^t dt' \, e^{\gamma(2t')/m} \left(\int_0^t dt'' \langle f(t')f(t'')\rangle\right)$$

$$= \int_0^t dt' \, e^{\gamma(2t')/m} \quad (a) \tag{7.18}$$

where we have defined the area under the curve as,

$$\int_0^t dt'' \langle f(t')f(t'')\rangle \approx \int_{-\infty}^{\infty} dt'' \langle f(t')f(t'')\rangle$$

$$= a \tag{7.19}$$

It follows that,

$$\langle v^2(t)\rangle = e^{-2\gamma t/m}\left[v^2(0) + \frac{a}{m^2}\int_0^t dt' \, e^{2\gamma t'/m}\right]$$

$$= e^{-2\gamma t/m}\left[v^2(0) + \frac{a}{m^2}\left(\frac{1}{2\gamma/m}\right)e^{2\gamma t/m}\Big|_0^t\right]$$

$$= e^{-2\gamma t/m}\left[v^2(0) + \frac{a}{2\gamma m}e^{2\gamma t/m} - \frac{a}{2\gamma m}\right]$$

$$= e^{-2\gamma t/m}\left(v^2(0) - \frac{a}{2\gamma m}\right) + \left(\frac{a}{2\gamma m}\right) \tag{7.20}$$

After a very long time $t \to \infty$, the mean square velocity $\langle v^2\rangle$ is,

$$\lim_{t\to\infty}\langle v^2(t)\rangle = \frac{a}{2\gamma m} \tag{7.21}$$

But it must also be consistent with the equipartition theorem of energy. Thus,

$$\frac{a}{2\gamma m} = \frac{k_B T}{m} \tag{7.22}$$

leading to the relation $a = 2\gamma k_B T$. This relationship between the friction coefficient γ and the magnitude of the random force (more precisely the autocorrelation function of the random force) is one of the formulations of the fluctuation-dissipation theorem.

7.4 Diffusional regime

During the diffusive spread of a substance in space, on average, there is no net displacement. There is no ballistic motion in which the net displacement is proportional to the velocity and the time. The position of the particle at time t is simply given by the integral of the velocity $v(t)$,

$$x(t) = x(0) + \int_0^t v(t')\, dt' \tag{7.23}$$

$$\left\langle (x(t) - x(0))^2 \right\rangle = \int_0^t dt' \int_0^t dt''\, \langle v(t')v(t'') \rangle \tag{7.24}$$

For a stationary system, we know that the velocity autocorrelation function $\langle v(t')v(t'') \rangle$ is an invariant by time translation and can be expressed as $C_v(t' - t'')$. As illustrated in Figure 7.7, we can do a change of variables for the double integral in Eq. (7.24) $\tau = t' - t''$ and $t^* = (t' + t'')/2$,

$$\left\langle (x(t) - x(0))^2 \right\rangle = \int_{-t}^t d\tau \int_{\frac{1}{2}|\tau|}^{t - \frac{1}{2}|\tau|} dt^*\, C_v(\tau)$$

$$= \int_{-t}^t d\tau\, C_v(\tau)\, (t - |\tau|)$$

$$= 2t \left[\int_0^t d\tau\, C_v(\tau) \right] - \int_{-t}^t d\tau\, C_v(\tau)\, |\tau| \tag{7.25}$$

the last term becomes negligible when the time is very large. Thus,

$$\lim_{t \to \infty} \frac{1}{2t} \left\langle (x(t) - x(0))^2 \right\rangle = \int_0^\infty \langle v(t)v(0) \rangle\, dt$$

$$= D \tag{7.26}$$

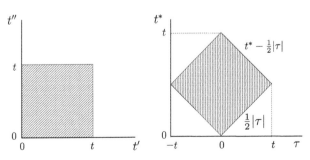

Fig. 7.7 Change of integration variables $\tau = t' - t''$ limit $t^* = (t' + t'')/2$ for the double integral in Eq. (7.24).

The constant D is the diffusion coefficient. This expression is general and valid for any dynamical system, as long as a long-time diffusional state exists. We can determine the diffusion coefficient obtained from the Langevin equation by integrating $\langle v(t)v(0)\rangle$ given in Eq. (7.38):

$$D = \int_0^\infty \langle v^2(0)\rangle \, e^{-\gamma t'/m} dt'$$

$$= \left(\frac{k_B T}{m}\right) \frac{1}{(\gamma/m)}$$

$$= \frac{k_B T}{\gamma} \tag{7.27}$$

The last equation is called the Einstein relation. It is another manifestation of the fluctuation-dissipation theorem.

7.5 Brownian dynamics

A simple generalization of the Langevin equation introduces an external force in addition to the dissipative friction and the random force,

$$m\frac{dv}{dt} = F(x) - \gamma v + f(t) \tag{7.28}$$

where the systematic force is typically determined from the gradient of a potential, $F(x) = -W'(x)$. To be consistent with the expected equilibrium behavior, the force acting on the particle should be calculated from the potential mean force (PMF). The random force $f(t)$ is assumed to satisfy the fluctuation-dissipation relation that we derived previously. A very appealing and simple approximation is obtained if it is assumed that the effect of the friction is large and that the inertial term associated with the acceleration, mdv/dt, is negligible. We then obtain the following equation of motion,

$$\gamma v = F + f(t)$$

$$v = \frac{F(x)}{\gamma} + \frac{f(t)}{\gamma}$$

$$\frac{dx}{dt} = \frac{D}{k_B T}F(x) + r(t) \tag{7.29}$$

where the Einstein relation from Eq. (7.27) was used. This approximation is what is commonly referred to as "Brownian dynamics" [Ermak (1975)].

It may be noted that the mass of the diffusing particle does not appear in the noninertial high friction limit. Here, the random kick $r(t)$ has the following properties,

$$\langle r(t) r(0) \rangle = \frac{\langle f(t) f(0) \rangle}{\gamma^2}$$

$$= \frac{2\gamma k_{\mathrm{B}} T}{\gamma^2} \delta(t)$$

$$= 2D\,\delta(t) \tag{7.30}$$

Dynamic evolution over a short time Δt is

$$\int_0^{\Delta t} dt' \frac{dx}{dt} = \int_0^{\Delta t} dt' \frac{D}{k_{\mathrm{B}} T} F(x) + \int_0^{\Delta t} dt'\, r(t')$$

$$\Delta x = \frac{D}{k_{\mathrm{B}} T} F(x) \Delta t + \int_0^{\Delta t} dt'\, r(t') \tag{7.31}$$

The displacement $\Delta x = x(\Delta t) - x(0)$ is a Gaussian-distributed variable characterized by its first two moments — the average and the mean square deviation. The average displacement is

$$\int_0^{\Delta t} dt' \frac{dx}{dt} = \int_0^{\Delta t} dt' \frac{D}{k_{\mathrm{B}} T} F(x) + \int_0^{\Delta t} dt'\, r(t')$$

$$\langle \Delta x \rangle = \frac{D}{k_{\mathrm{B}} T} F(x) \Delta t \tag{7.32}$$

because $\langle r(t') \rangle = 0$, and the mean square deviation is,

$$\langle \Delta x^2 \rangle = \int_0^{\Delta t} dt' \int_0^{\Delta t} dt''\, \langle r(t') r(t'') \rangle$$

$$= \int_0^{\Delta t} dt'\, 2D$$

$$= 2D\Delta t \tag{7.33}$$

Thus, the systematic displacement is accompanied by a small random diffusional step with mean square displacement equal to $2D\Delta t$.

7.6   Analysis from power spectrum

The Langevin equation represents a stationary stochastic process with no origin in time, that is, $t \in (-\infty, \infty)$. This means that we can examine the velocity autocorrelation function $C_v(t)$ by utilizing the Wiener–Khinchin theorem. This is sometimes referred to as the Rice power spectra method.

The Fourier transform of the Langevin equation is,

$$m(+i\omega)\widetilde{v}(\omega) = -\gamma\widetilde{v}(\omega) + \widetilde{f}(\omega) \tag{7.34}$$

such that

$$\widetilde{v}(\omega) = \frac{\widetilde{f}(\omega)}{mi\omega + \gamma} \tag{7.35}$$

The power spectrum of the velocity autocorrelation function is

$$\widetilde{C_v}(\omega) = \lim_{\mathcal{T}\to\infty} \frac{\|\widetilde{v}(\omega)\|^2}{2\mathcal{T}}$$

$$= \lim_{\mathcal{T}\to\infty} \left(\frac{1}{m^2\omega^2 + \gamma^2}\right) \frac{\left\|\widetilde{f}(\omega)\right\|^2}{2\mathcal{T}}$$

$$= \left(\frac{1}{m^2\omega^2 + \gamma^2}\right) \int_{-\infty}^{\infty} \langle f(t)f(0)\rangle \, e^{i\omega t} dt$$

$$= \left(\frac{1}{m^2\omega^2 + \gamma^2}\right) a \tag{7.36}$$

The velocity autocorrelation function is obtained by calculating the inverse Fourier transform,

$$C_v(t) = \frac{a}{2\gamma m} e^{-\gamma|t|/m} \tag{7.37}$$

and, again, we see that $a = 2\gamma k_\mathrm{B}T$ to satisfy that

$$C_v(t) = \langle v^2\rangle \, e^{-\gamma|t|/m} \tag{7.38}$$

The relationship can also be clarified by starting from the Fourier transform of the velocity autocorrelation function,

$$\widetilde{C_v}(\omega) = \mathscr{R}\left\{2\int_0^\infty dt \, e^{i\omega t} \langle v^2\rangle e^{-\gamma t/m}\right\}$$

$$= \mathscr{R}\left\{\frac{-2}{i\omega - \gamma/m}\right\}\langle v^2\rangle$$

$$= -2\mathscr{R}\left\{\frac{-i\omega - \gamma/m}{\omega^2 + \gamma^2/m^2}\right\}\langle v^2\rangle$$

$$= \frac{2\gamma/m}{(\omega^2 + \gamma^2/m^2)}\left(\frac{k_\mathrm{B}T}{m}\right)$$

$$= \left(\frac{2\gamma k_\mathrm{B}T}{m^2\omega^2 + \gamma^2}\right) \tag{7.39}$$

and again we see that $a = 2\gamma k_\mathrm{B}T$.

As a second example of this powerful technique, let us consider the Langevin equation for the harmonic oscillator. The Fourier transform of the Langevin equation is,

$$mi\omega\tilde{v}(\omega) = -\frac{K}{i\omega}\tilde{v}(\omega) - \gamma\tilde{v}(\omega) + \tilde{f}(\omega) \tag{7.40}$$

where

$$\tilde{x}(\omega) = \int_{-T}^{+T} dt'\, x(t')\, e^{-i\omega t'}$$

$$= \frac{1}{i\omega}\tilde{v}(\omega) \tag{7.41}$$

It follows that

$$\tilde{v}(\omega) = \tilde{f}(\omega)\, \frac{1}{mi\omega + \frac{K}{i\omega} + \gamma} \tag{7.42}$$

The power spectrum of the velocity autocorrelation function is

$$\tilde{C}_v(\omega) = \frac{2k_{\rm B}T\gamma}{m^2}\, \frac{\omega^2}{(\omega^2 - \omega_0^2)^2 + \omega^2(\gamma/m)^2} \tag{7.43}$$

where the natural frequency of the harmonic oscillator is $\omega_0 = \sqrt{K/m}$. The function $\tilde{C}_v(\omega)$ peaks at the natural frequency ω_0. The velocity autocorrelation function is obtained by calculating the inverse Fourier transform. The inverse Fourier transform yields,

$$C_v(t) = \frac{k_{\rm B}T}{m}\, e^{-(\gamma/2m)t}\left(\cos(\Omega t) - \frac{(\gamma/2m)}{\Omega}\sin(\Omega t)\right) \tag{7.44}$$

where $\Omega = \sqrt{\omega_0^2 - (\gamma/2m)^2}$. This expression is based on the assumption that the friction is moderate, $\omega_0 > \gamma/2m$, and the dynamics is underdamped. When the friction γ becomes very large, the dynamics becomes overdamped (Brownian dynamics) and the frequency becomes imaginary, yielding a velocity time-correlation function that decays exponentially.

7.7 Generalized Langevin equation

The generalized Langevin equation (GLE) may be written as [Zwanzig (1965); Kubo (1966)],

$$m\frac{dv(t)}{dt} = F_{\rm ext}(t) - \int_{-\infty}^{t} dt'\, M(t - t')v(t') + f(t) \tag{7.45}$$

where $F_{ext}(t)$ is an external time-dependent force. The main difference with the classical Langevin equation is the convolution in the time domain of the particle's velocity with a memory function $M(t)$ (also called the friction kernel). On average, this term gives rise to a dragging force opposing the movement of the particles. Lastly, there is also a time-dependent random force, $f(t)$, acting on the reduced system. The amplitude of $f(t)$ is typically assumed to be Gaussian-distributed, with $\langle f(t) \rangle = 0$ and $\langle f(t)f(0) \rangle = k_B T M(t)$. This can be demonstrated by examining the average response to an external time-dependent force,

$$m\frac{d\langle v(t) \rangle}{dt} = F_{ext}(t) - \int_{-\infty}^{t} M(t - t')\langle v(t') \rangle \, dt' \qquad (7.46)$$

Taking the Fourier transform on both sides yields,

$$\langle \tilde{v}(\omega) \rangle = \tilde{\mu}(\omega) \, \widetilde{F}_{ext}(\omega) \qquad (7.47)$$

with

$$\langle \tilde{v}(\omega) \rangle = \int_{-\infty}^{\infty} \langle v(t) \rangle \, e^{-i\omega t} \, dt \qquad (7.48)$$

and

$$\widetilde{F}_{ext}(\omega) = \int_{-\infty}^{\infty} F_{ext}(t) \, e^{-i\omega t} \, dt \qquad (7.49)$$

The frequency-dependent mobility $\tilde{\mu}(\omega)$ denotes the expected average linear response from the system:

$$\tilde{\mu}(\omega) = \frac{1}{mi\omega + \widetilde{M}(\omega)} \qquad (7.50)$$

with

$$\widetilde{M}(\omega) = \int_{0}^{\infty} M(t) \, e^{-i\omega t} \, dt \qquad (7.51)$$

It should be noted that $\widetilde{M}(\omega)$ denotes a Laplace–Fourier transform here because time–causality, that is, the relationship between a cause (happening at some point in time) and effect (taking place at a later point in time), is implicitly built in the condition that $M(t) = 0$ if $t < 0$ through the time convolution in Eq. (7.45). The same observation applies to the frequency-dependent mobility $\tilde{\mu}(\omega)$, which represents the mean mechanical response of the system to an external force. A useful relation between $\widetilde{M}(\omega)$ and $\widetilde{\mu}(\omega)$ can be derived by considering,

$$\widetilde{M}(\omega) = \frac{1}{\widetilde{\mu}(\omega)} - mi\omega$$

$$\mathscr{R}\left\{\widetilde{M}(\omega)\right\} = \mathscr{R}\left\{\frac{1}{\widetilde{\mu}(\omega)} - mi\omega\right\}$$

$$= \mathscr{R}\left\{\frac{1}{\widetilde{\mu}(\omega)}\frac{\widetilde{\mu}^*(\omega)}{\widetilde{\mu}^*(\omega)} - mi\omega\right\}$$

$$= \frac{1}{||\widetilde{\mu}(\omega)||^2}\mathscr{R}\left\{\widetilde{\mu}(\omega)\right\} \tag{7.52}$$

However, from the theory of linear response, we also know that

$$\widetilde{\mu}(\omega) = \frac{1}{k_{\mathrm{B}}T}\,\widetilde{C}_v(\omega) \tag{7.53}$$

where $\widetilde{C}_v(\omega)$ is the Laplace–Fourier transform of the velocity autocorrelation function. Accordingly, the velocity autocorrelation function from a physically correct GLE must satisfy this condition with respect to $\widetilde{\mu}(\omega)$. Eqs. (7.52) and (7.53) can be combined to yield,

$$\mathscr{R}\left\{\widetilde{C}_v(\omega)\right\} = k_{\mathrm{B}}T\,\mathscr{R}\left\{\widetilde{\mu}(\omega)\right\}$$

$$= k_{\mathrm{B}}T\,||\widetilde{\mu}(\omega)||^2\,\mathscr{R}\left\{\widetilde{M}(\omega)\right\} \tag{7.54}$$

Assuming stationary conditions, we can use the Wiener–Khinchin theorem and the method of Rice to calculate the velocity autocorrelation function generated by the GLE,

$$\lim_{\mathcal{T}\to\infty}\frac{||\widetilde{v}_{\mathcal{T}}(\omega)||^2}{2\mathcal{T}} = ||\widetilde{\mu}(\omega)||^2\,\lim_{\mathcal{T}\to\infty}\frac{||\widetilde{f}_{\mathcal{T}}(\omega)||^2}{2\mathcal{T}}$$

$$2\mathscr{R}\left\{\widetilde{C}_v(\omega)\right\} = ||\widetilde{\mu}(\omega)||^2\,2\mathscr{R}\left\{\widetilde{C}_f(\omega)\right\} \tag{7.55}$$

where we have expressed the Fourier transforms ($t \in [-\infty, +\infty]$) of $\langle v(t)v(0)\rangle$ and $\langle f(t)f(0)\rangle$ as two times the real part of their respective Laplace–Fourier transforms $\widetilde{C}_v$ and $\widetilde{C}_f$. Imposing that the $\widetilde{C}_v(\omega)$ associated with the linear-response (LR) mobility based on Eq. (7.54) be consistent with the $\widetilde{C_v}(\omega)$ of the stationary GLE dynamics based on Eq. (7.55),

$$\mathscr{R}\left\{\widetilde{C_v}(\omega)\right\} \text{ from LR} = \mathscr{R}\left\{\widetilde{C_v}(\omega)\right\} \text{ from GLE}$$

$$k_{\mathrm{B}}T \, ||\widetilde{\mu}(\omega)||^2 \, \mathscr{R}\left\{\widetilde{M}(\omega)\right\} = ||\widetilde{\mu}(\omega)||^2 \, \mathscr{R}\left\{\widetilde{C_f}(\omega)\right\}$$

$$k_{\mathrm{B}}T \, \mathscr{R}\left\{\widetilde{M}(\omega)\right\} = \mathscr{R}\left\{\widetilde{C_f}(\omega)\right\} \tag{7.56}$$

The condition imposed by Eq. (7.56) is equivalent to $k_{\mathrm{B}}T M(t) = \langle f(t)f(0)\rangle$, for $t > 0$. The relationship between the frequency-dependent random force and the memory function is a manifestation of the second fluctuation-dissipation theorem encountered in Eq. (6.84). The memory function is expected to decay rapidly compared to all other timescales in the system. The Markov assumption consists of making the approximation that the memory function decays instantaneously, that is, $M(t) \propto \delta(t)$, compared to all relevant timescales in the system,

$$-\int_0^t dt' \, M(t - t')v(t') \approx -v(t) \int_0^\infty dt' \, M(t - t')$$

$$\approx -\gamma \, v(t) \tag{7.57}$$

where γ is the friction coefficient:

$$\gamma = \int_0^\infty dt \, M(t)$$

$$= \frac{1}{k_{\mathrm{B}}T} \int_0^\infty dt \, \langle f(t)f(0)\rangle \tag{7.58}$$

This short-memory Markov assumption leads to the classical Langevin Eq. (7.14), which we have examined previously. The fluctuation-dissipation theorem then implies that $\langle f(t)f(0)\rangle = 2\gamma k_{\mathrm{B}}T \, \delta(t)$.

GLE for a particle in a harmonic potential

The dynamics of a particle of mass m in a harmonic potential can be examined in the context of the GLE,

$$m\frac{dv(t)}{dt} = -m\omega_0^2 x - \int_0^t M(t') \, \dot{x}(t - t') \, dt' + f(t) \tag{7.59}$$

where $\omega_0^2 = K/m$ is the natural frequency of the harmonic oscillator, and memory function $M(t)$ satisfies the fluctuation-dissipation relation,

$$M(t) = \frac{1}{k_{\mathrm{B}}T} \langle f(t+t')f(t') \rangle \, \Theta(t) \tag{7.60}$$

where $\Theta(t)$ is a Heaviside step-function equal to 1, when $t \geq 0$. Using the Laplace transform of the GLE, we write,

$$\mathcal{L}[v] = -x_0 + s\mathcal{L}[x]$$
$$\mathcal{L}[\dot{v}] = -v_0 + s\mathcal{L}[v]$$
$$\mathcal{L}[\ddot{x}] = -v_0 + s\mathcal{L}[v] = -v_0 + s(-x_0 + s\mathcal{L}[x]) \tag{7.61}$$

which leads to,

$$-v_0 + s\left(-x_0 + s\widetilde{x}(s)\right) = -\omega_0^2\, \widetilde{x}(s) - \frac{\widetilde{M}(s)}{m}\left(-x_0 + s\widetilde{x}(s)\right) + \frac{\widetilde{f}(s)}{m}$$

$$\widetilde{x}(s) = x_0 \frac{s + \widetilde{M}(s)/m}{\Delta(s)} + v_0\frac{1}{\Delta(s)} + \frac{\widetilde{f}(s)}{m}\frac{1}{\Delta(s)}$$

$$= x_0\, \widetilde{C}_{11}(s) + v_0\, \widetilde{C}_{12}(s) + \frac{\widetilde{f}(s)}{m}\frac{1}{\Delta(s)} \tag{7.62}$$

where $\Delta(s) = (\omega_0^2 + s^2 + s\widetilde{M}(s)/m)$. We also have that,

$$\widetilde{v}(s) = -x_0 + s\widetilde{x}(s)$$

$$= x_0 \frac{-\omega_0^2}{\Delta(s)} + v_0\frac{s}{\Delta(s)} + \widetilde{r}(s)\frac{s}{\Delta(s)}$$

$$= x_0\, \widetilde{C}_{21}(s) + v_0\, \widetilde{C}_{22}(s) + \frac{\widetilde{f}(s)}{m}\frac{s}{\Delta(s)} \tag{7.63}$$

It is useful to express the coefficient $\widetilde{C}_{ij}$ in matrix form,

$$\widetilde{\mathbf{C}}(s) = \begin{pmatrix} \widetilde{C}_{11} & \widetilde{C}_{12} \\ \widetilde{C}_{21} & \widetilde{C}_{22} \end{pmatrix}$$

$$= \frac{1}{\Delta(s)} \begin{pmatrix} s + \widetilde{M}(s)/m & 1 \\ -\omega_0^2 & s \end{pmatrix} \tag{7.64}$$

with $C_{11}(0) = 1$, $C_{12}(0) = 0$, $C_{21}(0) = 0$, and $C_{22}(0) = 1$. From this solution, the following relations are satisfied:

$$\dot{C}_{11}(t) = C_{21}(t) \tag{7.65}$$

$$\dot{C}_{12}(t) = C_{22}(t) \tag{7.66}$$

$$C_{21}(t) = -\omega_0^2\, C_{12}(t) \tag{7.67}$$

$$\dot{C}_{21}(t) = -\omega_0^2\, C_{22}(t) \tag{7.68}$$

The general solution can also be used to construct the relation:

$$\frac{1}{m} s\widetilde{M}(s)\widetilde{C}_{12}(s) + \widetilde{C}_{22}(s) = \widetilde{C}_{11}(s) \tag{7.69}$$

which is equivalent to the identity:

$$\frac{1}{m} \int_0^t dt'\, M(t - t')C_{12}(t') = C_{11}(t) - C_{22}(t) \tag{7.70}$$

In the time domain, the position and velocity are

$$x(t) = x_0\, C_{11}(t) + v_0\, C_{12}(t) + \frac{1}{m} \int_0^t dt'\, C_{12}(t - t')\, f(t')$$

$$v(t) = x_0\, C_{21}(t) + v_0\, C_{22}(t) + \frac{1}{m} \int_0^t dt'\, C_{22}(t - t')\, f(t') \tag{7.71}$$

Because the random force $\langle f(t) \rangle = 0$, the mean position and velocity as a function of time are

$$\langle x(t) \rangle = x_0\, C_{11}(t) + v_0\, C_{12}(t)$$

$$\langle v(t) \rangle = x_0\, C_{21}(t) + v_0\, C_{22}(t) \tag{7.72}$$

It is also possible to determine the quadratic fluctuations of the position and velocities as a function of time. As an example, let us examine the mean square deviation of the position and velocity as a function of time,

$$Q_{11}(t) = \langle x^2(t) \rangle - \langle x(t) \rangle^2$$

$$= \left\langle \left(\frac{1}{m} \int_0^t dt'\, C_{12}(t')\, f(t - t')\, \frac{1}{m} \int_0^t dt''\, C_{12}(t'')\, f(t - t'') \right) \right\rangle$$

$$= \frac{1}{m^2} \int_0^t dt' \int_0^t dt''\, C_{12}(t')\, C_{12}(t'')\, \langle f(t - t') f(t - t'') \rangle \qquad (7.73)$$

where we can use the fluctuation-dissipation relation between the force time autocorrelation function and the memory function,

$$k_{\mathrm{B}}T\, M(t'' - t') = \langle f(t - t') f(t - t'') \rangle\, \Theta(t'' - t') \qquad (7.74)$$

to get:

$$Q_{11}(t) = 2\, \frac{k_{\mathrm{B}}T}{m} \int_0^t dt'\, C_{12}(t') \left[\frac{1}{m} \int_0^{t'} dt''\, C_{12}(t'')\, M(t'' - t') \right]$$

$$= 2\, \frac{k_{\mathrm{B}}T}{m} \int_0^t dt'\, C_{12}(t') \left[C_{11}(t') - C_{22}(t') \right]$$

$$= 2\, \frac{k_{\mathrm{B}}T}{m} \int_0^t dt' \left(\frac{-C_{21}(t')}{\omega_0^2} \right) C_{11}(t') - 2\, \frac{k_{\mathrm{B}}T}{m} \int_0^t dt'\, C_{12}(t')\, \dot{C}_{12}(t')$$

$$= -2\, \frac{k_{\mathrm{B}}T}{m\omega_0^2} \int_0^t dt'\, \dot{C}_{11}(t')\, C_{11}(t') - \frac{k_{\mathrm{B}}T}{m} (C_{12}(t))^2$$

$$= -\frac{k_{\mathrm{B}}T}{m\omega_0^2} \left((C_{11}(t))^2 - 1 \right) - \frac{k_{\mathrm{B}}T}{m} (C_{12}(t))^2 \qquad (7.75)$$

where Eq. (7.70) was used. Relying on a similar analysis, Tuckerman and Berne (1993) showed that the relaxation time τ of the energy of the oscillator is related to the cosine-Fourier transform of the memory function evaluated at the natural frequency of the Drude oscillator ω_0,

$$\frac{1}{\tau} = \frac{\widetilde{M}(\omega_0)}{m} \qquad (7.76)$$

According to this expression, the thermalization rate of the oscillator depends on the excitations arising from the surrounding bulk at the frequency ω_0.

Chapter 8

Diffusion and time evolution of probability distribution

In Chapter 7, the concept of reduced models comprising a small subset of degrees of freedom was introduced. We saw that these reduced models evolve according to some effective nondeterministic stochastic dynamics to mimic the influence of the degrees of freedom that are left out. The reduced model serves to generate an ensemble of random trajectories that, in turn, can be used to calculate different types of averages. An alternative representation of outcome is through the evolution of a time-dependent probability distribution. In this case, the averaging process is exploited to construct a differential equation to calculate the evolution of the time-dependent probability distribution. While the two representations are formally equivalent, the latter often provides a more convenient route to derive closed-form expressions for important properties of the reduced model. This is the focus of this chapter.

8.1 Smoluchowski diffusion equation

Using some simple intuitive arguments, one can write a diffusion equation for a particle submitted to an effective potential. We have seen previously in Section 7.2 that a particle under the influence of a force F and frictional drag rapidly reaches an average drift velocity v_{drift}. The flux associated with this drift is,

$$J_{\text{drift}} = v_{\text{drift}} \, P$$

$$= \frac{F}{\gamma} P \tag{8.1}$$

There is also another flux, this one arising from the diffusive process (Fick's law):

$$J_{\text{diff}} = -D \frac{\partial P(x,t)}{\partial x} \tag{8.2}$$

The total flux is

$$J_{\text{tot}} = J_{\text{drift}} + J_{\text{diff}} = \frac{F}{\gamma} P - D \frac{\partial P}{\partial x} \tag{8.3}$$

If $P(x,0) = P_{\text{eq}}(x) \propto e^{-W(x)/k_B T}$, then the total flux J_{tot} should be zero,

$$J_{\text{tot}} = -\frac{\partial W}{\partial x} \frac{1}{\gamma} P_{\text{eq}}(x) - D \left(\frac{\partial W}{\partial x} \right) \left(\frac{1}{k_B T} \right) P_{\text{eq}}(x)$$

$$0 = \left(-\frac{1}{\gamma} + \frac{D}{k_B T} \right) \frac{\partial W}{\partial x} P_{\text{eq}}(x)$$

$$= \left(-\frac{1}{\gamma} + \frac{D}{k_B T} \right) \tag{8.4}$$

This condition of zero net flux under equilibrium conditions enforces a relationship between the diffusion coefficient and the friction, $D = k_B T/\gamma$, which we previously introduced in Eq. (7.27). In fact, this is the original argument from Einstein. Using the conservation condition, we can write an equation for the evolution of the probability $P(x,t)$ for a particle undergoing a Brownian dynamics diffusive process with a potential,

$$\frac{\partial P}{\partial t} = -\frac{\partial}{\partial x} \left(-\frac{D}{k_B T} \frac{\partial W(x)}{\partial x} P(x,t) - D \frac{\partial P(x,t)}{\partial x} \right)$$

$$= \frac{\partial}{\partial x} \left[D \left(e^{-W(x)/k_B T} \frac{\partial}{\partial x} \left(P(x,t) e^{+W(x)/k_B T} \right) \right) \right] \tag{8.5}$$

This is the Smoluchowski diffusion equation [Smoluchowski (1916)]. Based on the last relation, it is clear that the Boltzmann distribution ($\propto e^{-W(x)/k_B T}$) is a stationary solution ($\partial P/\partial t = 0$). Here, we have constructed the Smoluchowski diffusion equation intuitively by combining the two processes that are taking place simultaneously. A more rigorous derivation can be established through the Kramers–Moyal expansion of the Chapman–Kolmogorov equation. Let us consider the Brownian dynamics equation,

$$\frac{dx}{dt} = \frac{D}{k_B T} F(x) + r(t) \tag{8.6}$$

where $F(x) = -\partial W(x)/\partial x$ is the systematic force, and $r(t)$ is a Gaussian random noise obeying $\langle r(t) r(0) \rangle = 2D\delta(t)$. Let $P(x,t)$ be the probability density to find the particle with a position x at time t. The Chapman–Kolmogorov equation is a statement that the probability at any time is the result of a microscopic transition process (with no memory):

$$P(x, t + \Delta t) = \int_{-\infty}^{+\infty} d(\Delta x) \, g_{\Delta t}(x - \Delta x; \Delta x) \, P(x - \Delta x, t) \qquad (8.7)$$

where $g_{\Delta t}(x - \Delta x; \Delta x)$ is the microscopic transition probability to make a random jump of Δx over the time interval Δt starting at $x - \Delta x$. The function $g_{\Delta t}(x - \Delta x; \Delta x)$ is a Gaussian distribution with the first and second moments given by,

$$M_1(x) = \int_{-\infty}^{+\infty} d(\Delta x) \, \Delta x \, g_{\Delta t}(x; \Delta x)$$

$$= \frac{D}{k_B T} F \Delta t$$

$$= -\frac{D}{k_B T} \frac{\partial W}{\partial x} \Delta t \qquad (8.8)$$

and

$$M_2(x) = \int_{-\infty}^{+\infty} d(\Delta x) \, \Delta x^2 \, g_{\Delta t}(x; \Delta x)$$

$$= 2D \, \Delta t \qquad (8.9)$$

Writing Eq. (8.7) as

$$P(x, t + \Delta t) = \int_{-\infty}^{+\infty} d(\Delta x) \, I(x - \Delta x) \qquad (8.10)$$

we carry out a Taylor expansion of the integrand $I(x - \Delta x) = I(x) - I'(x)\Delta x + \frac{1}{2}I''(x)\Delta x^2 + \cdots$. This procedure is called the Kramers–Moyal expansion of the Chapman–Kolmogorov equation. Keeping only the first-order terms in Δt yields

$$P(x, t) + \frac{\partial P}{\partial t} \Delta t + \cdots = \int_{-\infty}^{+\infty} d(\Delta x) \left[\Big(g_{\Delta t}(x; \Delta x) P(x, t) \Big) \right.$$

$$- \frac{\partial}{\partial x} \Big(g_{\Delta t}(x; \Delta x) P(x, t) \Big) \Delta x$$

$$\left. + \frac{1}{2} \frac{\partial^2}{\partial x^2} \Big(g_{\Delta t}(x; \Delta x) P(x, t) \Big) \Delta x^2 + \cdots \right] \qquad (8.11)$$

we integrate over the variable Δx (getting averages),

$$P(x,t) + \frac{\partial P}{\partial t}\Delta t + \cdots = P(x,t) - \frac{\partial}{\partial x}\Big(M_1(x)P(x,t)\Big)$$

$$+ \frac{1}{2}\frac{\partial^2}{\partial x^2}\Big(M_2(x)P(x,t)\Big) + \cdots \quad (8.12)$$

and

$$\frac{\partial P}{\partial t} = \frac{1}{\Delta t}\left[\frac{\partial}{\partial x}\Big(-M_1(x)P(x,t)\Big) + \frac{1}{2}\frac{\partial^2}{\partial x^2}\Big(M_2(x)P(x,t)\Big)\right]$$

$$= \frac{1}{\Delta t}\frac{\partial}{\partial x}\left[-M_1(x)P(x,t) + \frac{1}{2}\frac{\partial}{\partial x}\Big(M_2(x)P(x,t)\Big)\right]$$

$$= \frac{\partial}{\partial x}\left[\left(\frac{\partial W(x)}{\partial x}\frac{D}{k_B T}\right)P(x,t) + \frac{1}{2}\frac{\partial}{\partial x}\Big(2DP(x,t)\Big)\right]$$

$$= \frac{\partial}{\partial x}\left[\frac{\partial W(x)}{\partial x}\frac{D}{k_B T}P(x,t) + D\frac{\partial}{\partial x}P(x,t)\right]$$

$$= \frac{\partial}{\partial x}\left[D\left(e^{-W(x)/k_B T}\frac{\partial}{\partial x}\Big(P(x,t)e^{+W(x)/k_B T}\Big)\right)\right] \quad (8.13)$$

Based on the last relation, it is clear that the Boltzmann distribution $(\propto e^{-W(x)/k_B T})$ is a stationary solution $(\partial P/\partial t = 0)$. The flux is

$$J(x) = -\frac{\partial W(x)}{\partial x}\frac{D}{k_B T}P(x,t) - D\frac{\partial}{\partial x}P(x,t)$$

$$= J_{\text{drift}} + J_{\text{diff}} \quad (8.14)$$

which displays the drift and diffusion (Fick's law) contributions to the total flux.

Added note: Space-dependent diffusion coefficient $D(x)$
If the diffusion coefficient depends on the position, one has to be careful in determining the short time propagation. We first rewrite the Langevin equation $mdv(t)/dt = F(x) - \gamma(x)v(t) + f(t)$, as,

$$\frac{D(x)}{k_B T}m\frac{dv}{dt} + v(t) = \frac{D(x)}{k_B T}F(x) + r(t) \quad (8.15)$$

We then expand the space-dependent diffusion coefficient $D(x)$ locally, which we write as

$$D(x(t)) = D(x)\Big|_{x=x(0)} + \frac{\partial D(x)}{\partial x}\Big|_{x=x(0)}\Delta x(t)$$

$$D(x(t)) = D_0 + D_0'\,\Delta x(t) \quad (8.16)$$

Using this expression, we write:

$$\frac{D_0}{k_B T} m \frac{dv(t)}{dt} + v(t) = \frac{D_0}{k_B T} F - \frac{D_0'}{k_B T} m \Delta x \frac{dv}{dt} + r(t)$$

$$e^{-t/\tau_0} \frac{d}{dt}\left(e^{t/\tau_0} v\right) = \frac{D_0}{k_B T} F - \frac{D_0'}{k_B T} m \Delta x \frac{dv}{dt} + r(t)$$

$$\int_0^{\Delta t} v(t')dt' \approx \frac{D_0}{k_B T} \int_0^{\Delta t} F(t')dt' - \frac{D_0'}{k_B T} \int_0^{\Delta t} m \Delta x \frac{dv}{dt} dt' + \int_0^{\Delta t} r(t')dt'$$

$$\Delta x = \frac{D_0 F}{k_B T} \Delta t - \frac{D_0'}{k_B T} \int_0^{\Delta t} m\left(\frac{d}{dt}(\Delta x\, v) - v^2\right) dt' + \int_0^{\Delta t} r(t')dt'$$

$$\Delta x = \frac{D_0 F}{k_B T} \Delta t - D_0' \Delta t + \int_0^{\Delta t} r(t')dt' \tag{8.17}$$

where it was assumed that $\Delta t \ll \tau_0 = m k_B T / D_0$, and this transformation was used

$$\int_0^{\Delta t} m\left(\frac{d}{dt}(\Delta x\, v) - v^2\right) dt' = m \Delta x\, v \Big|_0^{\Delta t} - \int_0^{\Delta t} m v^2 dt'$$

$$= -m\left\langle v^2 \right\rangle \Delta t$$

$$= -k_B T \Delta t \tag{8.18}$$

As in the previous case, the displacement Δx is a Gaussian-distributed variable characterized by its first two moments. The first moment (average displacement) is

$$M_1(x) = \langle \Delta x \rangle$$

$$= \frac{D_0 F}{k_B T} \Delta t + D_0' \Delta t$$

$$= \left(-\frac{\partial W(x)}{\partial x} \frac{D(x)}{k_B T} + \frac{\partial D(x)}{\partial x}\right) \Delta t \tag{8.19}$$

where the last term is called the spurious drift [Ermak (1975)]. The second moment, $M_2(x) = 2D\Delta t$, keeps the same form. The time derivative of the probability distribution is,

$$\frac{\partial P}{\partial t} = \frac{1}{\Delta t} \frac{\partial}{\partial x}\left[-M_1(x)P(x,t) + \frac{1}{2}\frac{\partial}{\partial x}\left(M_2(x)P(x,t)\right)\right]$$

$$= \frac{\partial}{\partial x}\left[\left(\frac{\partial W(x)}{\partial x}\frac{D(x)}{k_B T} - \frac{\partial D(x)}{\partial x}\right) P(x,t) + \frac{1}{2}\frac{\partial}{\partial x}\left(2D(x)P(x,t)\right)\right]$$

$$= \frac{\partial}{\partial x}\left[\frac{\partial W(x)}{\partial x}\frac{D(x)}{k_B T} P(x,t) + D(x)\frac{\partial}{\partial x}P(x,t)\right]$$

$$= \frac{\partial}{\partial x}\left[D(x)\left(e^{-W(x)/k_B T}\frac{\partial}{\partial x}\left(P(x,t)e^{+W(x)/k_B T}\right)\right)\right] \tag{8.20}$$

8.2 Poisson-Nernst-Planck equation

The Smoluchowski diffusion equation can easily be generalized to multi-component in three dimensions:

$$\frac{\partial C_i(\mathbf{r}, t)}{\partial t} = \boldsymbol{\nabla} \cdot \left(\frac{D_i}{k_{\mathrm{B}} T} \boldsymbol{\nabla} W_i(\mathbf{r}) + D_i \boldsymbol{\nabla} C_i(\mathbf{r}, t) \right) \qquad (8.21)$$

where we have converted the probability P_i into a concentration C_i, based on the assumption that the tagged particles do not interfere too much with one another. One could utilize this equation to describe the diffusion of particles in the potential $W_i(\mathbf{r})$. An interesting particular case is the electrodiffusion of ions in solution. The potential W_i is then dominated by long-range electrostatics interactions, $W_i(\mathbf{r}, t) \equiv q_i \phi(\mathbf{r}, t)$, where $\phi(\mathbf{r}, t)$ is the average electrostatic potential. In principle, if the spatial concentration of the ions is known, one can calculate $\phi(\mathbf{r}, t)$ by using the macroscopic Poisson equation:

$$\boldsymbol{\nabla} \cdot (\epsilon(\mathbf{r}) \boldsymbol{\nabla} \phi(\mathbf{r}, t)) = -4\pi \rho_{\mathrm{solute}}(\mathbf{r}) - 4\pi \sum_i q_i C_i(\mathbf{r}, t) \qquad (8.22)$$

Coupling the diffusion equation to the macroscopic Poisson equation yields the Poisson-Nernst-Planck electrodiffusion theory. Typically, these equations are solved in tandem by iterating with a small time-step [Cardenas *et al.* (2000); Im and Roux (2002)]: assuming an initial concentration profile $C_i(\mathbf{r})$, the Poisson equation is solved to obtain the potential ϕ, the latter is then inserted into the Smoluchowski diffusion equation to determine the concentration some Δt later, and the process is repeated. When the ion distribution reaches equilibrium, the theory is reduced to the nonlinear Poisson–Boltzmann (PB) equation, which we have discussed in Chapter 4. Another situation can be encountered when the system is assumed to be in a nonequilibrium stationary state, such that the spatial concentrations are not changing with time.

8.3 Fokker–Planck equation

We would like to obtain a differential equation for $P(v, t)$, the probability density to find the particle with a velocity v at time t, for the Langevin equation,

$$\frac{dv}{dt} = -\frac{\gamma}{m} v + \frac{1}{m} f(t) \qquad (8.23)$$

where $f(t)$ is a Gaussian random noise obeying $\langle f(t) f(0) \rangle = 2\gamma k_{\mathrm{B}} T \delta(t)$. We have already derived the Smoluchowski diffusion equation using the

Kramers–Moyal expansion for a very similar problem. Let us consider the BD equation for a harmonic oscillator with force constant K,

$$\frac{dx}{dt} = -\frac{KD}{k_B T}x + r(t) \tag{8.24}$$

with $\langle r(t)r(0)\rangle = 2D\delta(t)$. By analogy with the previous analysis, we can see that BD and the Langevin equation are mathematically equivalent if:

$$x \to v$$
$$\frac{KD}{k_B T} \to \frac{\gamma}{m}$$
$$D \to \frac{\gamma k_B T}{m^2} \tag{8.25}$$

which implies that the Kramers–Moyal expansion of a Chapman–Kolmogorov equation will lead to,

$$\frac{\partial P(v,t)}{\partial t} = \frac{\partial}{\partial v}\left[v\frac{\gamma}{m}P(v,t) + \frac{\gamma k_B T}{m^2}\frac{\partial}{\partial v}P(v,t)\right]$$
$$= \frac{\gamma k_B T}{m^2}\frac{\partial}{\partial v}\left[\left(e^{-\frac{1}{2}mv^2/k_B T}\frac{\partial}{\partial v}\left(P(v,t)e^{+\frac{1}{2}mv^2/k_B T}\right)\right)\right] \tag{8.26}$$

This is the Fokker–Planck equation for the probability density of the velocity v. Here, $\gamma k_B T/m^2$ is the equivalent of the diffusion constant of the velocity. It is clear that the Maxwell distribution of velocity ($\propto e^{-\frac{1}{2}mv^2/k_B T}$) is a stationary solution ($\partial P/\partial t = 0$).

8.4 Chandrasekar equation

Let $P(x, v, t)$ be the joint probability density to find the particle at position x with a velocity v at time t. The Chapman–Kolmogorov equation is:

$$P(x, v, t + \Delta t) = \int_{-\infty}^{+\infty} d(\Delta x) \int_{-\infty}^{+\infty} d(\Delta v) \, \Phi_{\Delta t}(x - \Delta x, v - \Delta v; \Delta x, \Delta v)$$
$$\times P(x - \Delta x, v - \Delta v, t) \tag{8.27}$$

where $\Phi_{\Delta t}(x - \Delta x, v - \Delta v; \Delta x, \Delta v)$ is the microscopic transition probability to make a jump of Δx and Δv over the time interval Δt starting at $x - \Delta x$

and $v - \Delta v$. According to the Langevin equation,

$$m\frac{dv}{dt} = F - \gamma v + f(t) \tag{8.28}$$

where $F = -\partial W(x)/\partial x$ is assumed to be a systematic (conservative) force arising from the potential $W(x)$, and $f(t)$ is a zero-average Gaussian noise obeying the fluctuation-dissipation theorem, $\langle f(t)f(0)\rangle = 2k_{\mathrm{B}}T\delta(t)$. We can get the evolution of the system from its initial conditions at time t to a short time Δt later,

$$x(t + \Delta t) - x(t) = \Delta x$$
$$= v(t)\Delta t \tag{8.29}$$

and

$$v(t + \Delta t) - v(t) = \Delta v$$
$$= \frac{F}{m}\Delta t - \frac{\gamma}{m}v\Delta t + \frac{1}{m}\int_0^{\Delta t} f(t')\,dt' \tag{8.30}$$

The evolution of the position x is "deterministic" and depends only on the velocity. From this, it follows that the microscopic transition probability can be written as

$$\Phi_{\Delta t}(x, v; \Delta x, \Delta v) = \delta(\Delta x - v\Delta t)\, g_{\Delta t}(x, v; \Delta v) \tag{8.31}$$

where $g_{\Delta t}(x, v; \Delta v)$ is a Gaussian distribution with the first and second moments, M_1 and M_2,

$$M_1 = \langle \Delta v \rangle$$
$$= \int_{-\infty}^{+\infty} d(\Delta v)\, \Delta v\, g_{\Delta t}(x, v; \Delta v)$$
$$= \frac{F}{m}\Delta t - \frac{\gamma}{m}v\Delta t \tag{8.32}$$

and

$$M_2 = \langle \Delta v^2 \rangle$$
$$= \int_{-\infty}^{+\infty} d(\Delta v)\, \Delta v^2\, g_{\Delta t}(x, v; \Delta v)$$
$$= \frac{2\gamma k_{\mathrm{B}}T}{m^2}\Delta t \tag{8.33}$$

Using Eq. (8.31), we can easily integrate Eq. (8.27) over Δx to get:

$$P(x, v, t + \Delta t) = \int_{-\infty}^{+\infty} d(\Delta v) \; g_{\Delta t}(x - v\Delta t, v; \Delta v) \; P(x - v\Delta t, v - \Delta v, t)$$

(8.34)

We then shift the position in x by $+v\Delta t$:

$$P(x + v\Delta t, v, t + \Delta t) = \int_{-\infty}^{+\infty} d(\Delta v) \; g_{\Delta t}(x, v; \Delta v) \; P(x, v - \Delta v, t)$$

(8.35)

and carry out a Taylor expansion for small Δv around the point (x, v, t) on both sides,

$$P + \frac{\partial P}{\partial x} v\Delta t + \frac{\partial P}{\partial t} \Delta t + \cdots = \int_{-\infty}^{+\infty} d(\Delta v) \Big[(g_{\Delta t}(x, v; \Delta v) P(x, v, t))$$

$$- \frac{\partial}{\partial v} (g_{\Delta t}(x, v; \Delta v) P(x, v, t)) \Delta v$$

$$+ \frac{1}{2} \frac{\partial^2}{\partial v^2} (g_{\Delta t}(x, v; \Delta v) P(x, v, t)) \Delta v^2 + \cdots \Big]$$

$$P + \frac{\partial P}{\partial x} v\Delta t + \frac{\partial P}{\partial t} \Delta t + \cdots = P - \frac{\partial}{\partial v} (M_1 P) + \frac{1}{2} \frac{\partial^2}{\partial v^2} (M_2 P) + \cdots$$

$$\frac{\partial P}{\partial x} v\Delta t + \frac{\partial P}{\partial t} \Delta t + \cdots = -\frac{\partial}{\partial v} (M_1 P) + \frac{1}{2} \frac{\partial^2}{\partial v^2} (M_2 P) + \cdots \quad (8.36)$$

Keeping only the first-order terms in Δt and using the expressions for M_1 and M_2 we get,

$$\frac{\partial P}{\partial t} + \frac{\partial P}{\partial x} v = -\frac{\partial}{\partial v} \left(\left(\frac{F}{m} - \frac{\gamma}{m} v \right) P \right) + \frac{1}{2} \frac{\partial^2}{\partial v^2} \left(\frac{2\gamma k_B T}{m^2} P \right)$$

$$\frac{\partial P}{\partial t} + \frac{\partial P}{\partial x} v + \frac{\partial P}{\partial v} \frac{F}{m} = \frac{\gamma v}{m} \frac{\partial P}{\partial v} + \frac{\gamma}{m} P + \frac{\gamma k_B T}{m^2} \frac{\partial^2 P}{\partial v^2}$$

$$= \frac{\gamma}{m} \frac{\partial}{\partial v} \left\{ vP + \frac{k_B T}{m} \frac{\partial P}{\partial v} \right\}$$

$$= \frac{\gamma k_B T}{m^2} \frac{\partial}{\partial v} \left\{ e^{-\frac{1}{2}mv^2/k_B T} \frac{\partial}{\partial v} \left(Pe^{+\frac{1}{2}mv^2/k_B T} \right) \right\}$$

(8.37)

This equation was derived by Chandrasekar [Chandrasekar (1943)]. The l.h.s is the Liouville operator (total time derivative) acting on the probability density (with $\dot{x} = v$, and $\dot{v} = F/m$):

$$\mathbf{L} \equiv \frac{d}{dt}$$

$$= \frac{\partial}{\partial t} + \frac{\partial}{\partial x}\dot{x} + \frac{\partial}{\partial v}\dot{v}$$

$$= \frac{\partial}{\partial t} + \frac{\partial}{\partial x}\frac{p}{m} + \frac{\partial}{\partial v}\frac{F}{m} \tag{8.38}$$

So the equation can be written as

$$\mathbf{L}\,P = \frac{\gamma k_B T}{m^2}\,\frac{\partial}{\partial v}\left\{e^{-\frac{1}{2}mv^2/k_B T}\frac{\partial}{\partial v}\left(P e^{+\frac{1}{2}mv^2/k_B T}\right)\right\} \tag{8.39}$$

where the r.h.s is sometimes called the Fokker–Planck "collision" operator. If the friction γ is zero, then there are no collisions and the Chandrasekar equation represents only the streaming of the probability density arising from unperturbed classical trajectories. If the probability distribution is Maxwell–Boltzmann, then it is stationary and does not vary with time. Importantly, for any nonzero value of friction γ, the system over time relaxes toward the Maxwell–Boltzmann equilibrium distribution. Thus, while dissipative forces clearly affect dynamical and relaxation processes in the system, they do not alter the resulting equilibrium distribution.

Chapter 9

Transition rates

A situation where long timescales are important is when there are rare transitions between two stable states. While the fluctuations within the stable states may occur on a short timescale, the actual transitions between the stable states may take place on a far longer timescale. A typical case is illustrated in Figure 9.1 where two stable states, A and B, are separated by a large energy barrier. An important concept illustrated in Figure 9.1 is the identification of a "reaction coordinate," x, that can be used to monitor the progress of the transition. Theoretical analysis to determine the transition rate between stable states can vary greatly in sophistication and complexity. One of the simplest treatments goes back to transition state theory (TST).

9.1 Transition state theory

The issue is to determine the interconversion rates for the phenomenological process,

$$A \; \underset{k_{B \to A}}{\overset{k_{A \to B}}{\rightleftharpoons}} \; B$$

Starting from state A at time t, the total probability p of crossings from A to B during time interval Δt is,

$$p = \int_0^\infty dv \int_{x^\dagger - v\Delta t}^{x^\dagger} P(x, v) dx \tag{9.1}$$

The joint equilibrium probability $P(x, v)$ of having specific values for x and v at the same time is a simple product of two independent equilibrium

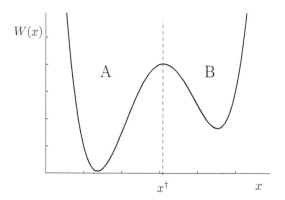

Fig. 9.1 Schematic representation of a system with two stable states, A and B, that are separated by a large energy barrier.

distributions: the marginal Boltzmann distribution $P_{\text{Boltzmann}}(x)$ for the position, and the Maxwell distribution $P_{\text{Maxwell}}(v)$ for the velocity,

$$P(x,v) = \frac{P_{\text{Boltzmann}}(x)}{\int_A dx\, P_{\text{Boltzmann}}(x)}\, P_{\text{Maxwell}}(v) \tag{9.2}$$

The normalization by the denominator ensures that we are counting configurations starting from the state A. The total probability p of crossings per unit of time is then,

$$
\begin{aligned}
k_{\text{A}\to\text{B}} &= \frac{p}{\Delta t} \\
&= \frac{1}{\Delta t}\int_0^\infty dv\, P_{\text{Maxwell}}(v)\left(\int_{x^\dagger - v\Delta t}^{x^\dagger} dx\, P_{\text{Boltzmann}}(x)\right) \\
&= \frac{1}{\Delta t}\int_0^\infty dv\, P_{\text{Maxwell}}(v)\left(P_{\text{Boltzmann}}(x^\dagger)(v\Delta t)\right) \\
&= P_{\text{Boltzmann}}(x^\dagger)\int_{-\infty}^\infty dv\, P_{\text{Maxwell}}(v)\, v\theta(v) \\
&= P_{\text{Boltzmann}}(x^\dagger)\,\langle v\theta(v)\rangle \tag{9.3}
\end{aligned}
$$

where $\theta(v)$ is a Heaviside step-function equal to 1, when $v > 0$, and zero, otherwise. The rate is equal to the total number of systems crossing the separatrix $x^\dagger$ from the reactant A to the product state B per unit of time, knowing that the system was initially in state A. The probability to find the system with $x = x^\dagger$ knowing that the system was known to be in the state A initially is,

$$P_{\text{Boltzmann}}(x^\dagger) = \frac{e^{-W(x^\dagger)/k_{\text{B}}T}}{\int_{-\infty}^{x^\dagger} e^{-W(x)/k_{\text{B}}T} dx} \tag{9.4}$$

It follows that the transition rate is,

$$k_{\text{A}\to\text{B}} = \frac{e^{-W(x^\dagger)/k_{\text{B}}T}}{\int_{-\infty}^{x^\dagger} e^{-W(x)/k_{\text{B}}T} dx} \langle v\theta(v) \rangle \tag{9.5}$$

This expression is the TST [Glasstone *et al.* (1941)]. This is equal to the probability density of the system at the separatrix, $P(x^\dagger)$ (i.e., the number of systems per unit of length), times the mean length traveled per unit of time by a forward-going system (i.e., the mean forward velocity $\langle v\theta(v) \rangle$). To obtain a final expression, it is necessary to define and evaluate a number of different terms. The mean forward velocity is

$$\langle v\theta(v) \rangle = \int_0^\infty dv\, v\, P_{\text{Maxwell}}(v)$$

$$= \left(\frac{m}{2\pi k_{\text{B}}T} \right)^{1/2} \int_0^\infty dv\, v\, e^{-mv^2/2k_{\text{B}}T}$$

$$= \left(\frac{m}{2\pi k_{\text{B}}T} \right)^{1/2} \int_0^\infty d\left(-\frac{k_{\text{B}}T}{m} e^{-mv^2/2k_{\text{B}}T} \right)$$

$$= \left(\frac{m}{2\pi k_{\text{B}}T} \right)^{1/2} \left(\frac{k_{\text{B}}T}{m} \right)$$

$$= \left(\frac{k_{\text{B}}T}{2\pi m} \right)^{1/2} \tag{9.6}$$

The integral in the denominator of Eq. (9.4) can be simplified by making some simple assumptions:

$$\int_{-\infty}^{x^\dagger} e^{-W(x)/k_{\text{B}}T} dx \approx \int_{-\infty}^{\infty} e^{-[W(x_{\text{A}})+\frac{1}{2}W''(x_{\text{A}})(x-x_{\text{A}})^2]/k_{\text{B}}T} dx$$

$$= \sqrt{2\pi k_{\text{B}}T/W''(x_{\text{A}})}\, e^{-W(x_{\text{A}})/k_{\text{B}}T}$$

$$\approx e^{-W(x_{\text{A}})/k_{\text{B}}T} \left(\frac{2\pi k_{\text{B}}T}{W''(x_{\text{A}})} \right)^{1/2} \tag{9.7}$$

where we have used a quadratic approximation near x_{min} at the bottom of the well, $W(x) \approx W(x_{\text{A}}) + \frac{1}{2}W''(x_{\text{A}})(x - x_{\text{min}})^2$. We then can insert this result in our expression above for the forward TST rate $k_{A \to B}$,

$$
\begin{aligned}
k_{A \to B} &= \frac{e^{-W(x^\dagger)/k_B T}}{\int_r dx \, e^{-W(x)/k_B T}} \times \langle v\theta(v) \rangle \\
&= e^{-[W(x^\dagger) - W(x_A)]/k_B T} \left(\frac{W''(x_A)}{2\pi k_B T} \right)^{1/2} \times \left(\frac{k_B T}{2\pi m} \right)^{1/2} \\
&= e^{-[W(x^\dagger) - W(x_A)]/k_B T} \frac{1}{2\pi} \left(\frac{W''(x_A)}{m} \right)^{1/2} \\
&= \nu \, e^{-\Delta W^\dagger/k_B T}
\end{aligned}
\tag{9.8}
$$

where $\Delta W^\dagger = W(x^\dagger) - W(x_A)$ is the activation free energy, and $\nu = \sqrt{W''(x_A)/m}/2\pi$ is the oscillation frequency of a particle of mass m at the bottom of the well A with curvature $W''(x_A)$. This expression is Eyring rate theory. The backward TST rate $k_{B \to A}$ can be deduced from the forward rate and the ratio of the equilibrium probabilities $P_A k_{A \to B} = P_B k_{B \to A}$. Several textbooks write the TST rate as,

$$
k_{A \to B}^{(TST)} = \frac{k_B T}{h} e^{-\Delta W^*/k_B T}
\tag{9.9}
$$

where h is Planck's constant $(6.63 \times 10^{-34} \text{ J·s})$. This expression was derived for quantum mechanical processes occurring in the gas phase. The expression is equivalent if we write that $\Delta W^* = \Delta W^\dagger + \ln(h\nu/k_B T)$.

9.2 Reactive flux formalism

The TST transition rate assumes that the particle is undergoing pure ballistic motion $x(t) = x(0) + v(0)t$, when it attempts to cross the top of the barrier. As a result, the TST transition rate in Eq. (9.5) comprises only the average forward velocity, with no influence on the trajectory from the surrounding environment. In reality, the dynamics of the particle is going to be more complicated due to the interactions with the surrounding environment and also, dissipative factors should play a role. These issues can be addressed by deriving a more general expression for the transition rate constant. To begin, let us introduce the step-function population operators $H_A(x)$ and $H_B(x)$, which are equal to 1, when the system is in state A or B, and zero, otherwise. The conditional probability that the system will be found in state B at time t, assuming it was initially in state A at $t = 0$,

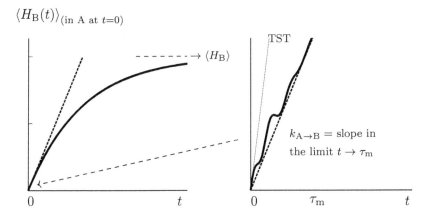

Fig. 9.2 Time evolution of $\langle H_B(t)\rangle_{(\text{in A at } t=0)}$, the conditional probability that the system will be found in state B at time t, assuming it was initially in state A at $t = 0$. On the left is the evolution of $\langle H_B(t)\rangle_{(\text{in A at } t=0)}$ over a macroscopic time. Assuming the overall exponential relaxation dependence, $\langle H_B(t)\rangle_{(\text{in A at } t=0)}$ goes to $\to \langle H_B\rangle$ after a very long time. The curve on the right is focused on the initial evolution of $\langle H_B(t)\rangle_{(\text{in A at } t=0)}$ over a microscopic time. The transition rate $k_{A\to B}$ is equal to the slope of the conditional probability in the limit of $t \to \tau_m$, where τ_m represents a microscopic relaxation timescale. The TST rate from Eq. (9.5) is equal to the initial slope of the conditional probability in the limit of $t \to 0^+$.

can be written as,

$$\langle H_B(t)\rangle_{(\text{in A at } t=0)} = \frac{\langle H_A(0)H_B(t)\rangle}{\langle H_A\rangle} \tag{9.10}$$

The expected time evolution of this conditional probability is illustrated in Figure 9.2. It should start at 0 at $t =$ and relax after a long time to the equilibrium population of the state B, $\langle H_B\rangle$. After some rapid relaxation over a microscopic timescale τ_m, the initial slope of the conditional probability should reflect the first-order rate process. The time τ_m represents the timescale of molecular dissipative and collisional relaxation taking place at the transition state before the barrier crossing is completed. For the existence of a rate constant, the molecular relaxation time τ_m should be much smaller than the timescale implied by the rate constant, $1/k_{A\to B}$. Accordingly,

$$k_{A\to B} = \lim_{t\to\tau_m} \frac{d}{dt} \frac{\langle H_A(0)H_B(t)\rangle}{\langle H_A\rangle}$$

$$= \lim_{t\to\tau_m} \frac{1}{\langle H_A\rangle} \left\langle H_A(0)\dot{H}_B(t)\right\rangle$$

$$= \lim_{t \to \tau_{\mathrm{m}}} \ -\frac{1}{\langle H_{\mathrm{A}} \rangle} \left\langle \dot{H}_{\mathrm{A}}(0) H_{\mathrm{B}}(t) \right\rangle$$

$$= \lim_{t \to \tau_{\mathrm{m}}} \frac{1}{\langle H_{\mathrm{A}} \rangle} \left\langle \delta(x(0) - x^{\dagger})\, v(0)\, H_{\mathrm{B}}(t) \right\rangle$$

$$= \frac{1}{\langle H_{\mathrm{A}} \rangle} \left\langle \delta(x(0) - x^{\dagger})\, v(0)\, H_{\mathrm{B}}(\tau_{\mathrm{m}}) \right\rangle$$

$$= \frac{1}{\langle H_{\mathrm{A}} \rangle} \left\langle \delta(x - x^{\dagger}) \right\rangle \frac{\left\langle \delta(x - x^{\dagger})\, v\, \theta(v) \right\rangle}{\left\langle \delta(x - x^{\dagger}) \right\rangle} \frac{\left\langle \delta(x(0) - x^{\dagger})\, v(0)\, H_{\mathrm{B}}(\tau_{\mathrm{m}}) \right\rangle}{\left\langle \delta(x - x^{\dagger})\, v\, \theta(v) \right\rangle}$$

$$= \underbrace{\frac{e^{-W(x^{\dagger})/k_{\mathrm{B}}T}}{\int_{-\infty}^{x^{\dagger}} e^{-W(x)/k_{\mathrm{B}}T}\, dx} \quad \langle v\, \theta(v) \rangle}_{k_{\mathrm{TST}}} \quad \times \quad \underbrace{\kappa}_{\text{transmission coefficient}}$$

$$(9.11)$$

where we have used the relations:

$$\left\langle H_{\mathrm{A}}(0) \dot{H}_{\mathrm{B}}(t) \right\rangle = -\left\langle \dot{H}_{\mathrm{A}}(0) H_{\mathrm{B}}(t) \right\rangle$$

and

$$\frac{d}{dt} H_{\mathrm{A}}(x) = \frac{dH_{\mathrm{A}}}{dx} \frac{dx}{dt}$$

$$= -\delta(x - x^{\dagger})\, v \qquad (9.12)$$

(the slope is negative because the indicator function goes from 1 to zero from state A to state B). This statistical mechanical treatment of the transition rate is called "reactive flux formalism" [Chandler (1978)]. The transmission coefficient $\kappa(t)$ is a correlation function that monitors the rapid back-and-forth interconversions (i.e., "recrossings") and complex dynamics of the particle near the top of the free energy barrier. At a very short time, $\kappa(0^{+}) = 1$, but then is expected to rapidly relax to a plateau value after a microscopic time interval τ_{m}. For TST, κ is assumed to be equal to 1, but in general, $0 \leq \kappa \leq 1$. The transmission coefficient includes the deviation of $k_{\mathrm{A} \to \mathrm{B}}$ from the classical TST rate due to the dissipative and collisional recrossing effects taking place during the transitions. It can be calculated from the reactive flux correlation function from an ensemble of activated dynamics trajectories generated from a biased position–velocity distribution function $P^{(+)}(\Gamma)$,

$$P^{(+)}(\Gamma) = \frac{v\,\theta(v)\,\delta(x - x^\dagger)\,\mathrm{e}^{-\mathcal{H}(\Gamma)/k_\mathrm{B}T}}{\int d\Gamma\,v\,\theta(v)\,\delta(x - x^\dagger)\,\mathrm{e}^{-\mathcal{H}(\Gamma)/k_\mathrm{B}T}} \tag{9.13}$$

where $\mathcal{H}(\Gamma)$ is the Hamiltonian and Γ represents all the degrees of freedom, coordinates and momenta, in the system. It follows that the transmission coefficient may be calculated as,

$$\kappa = \lim_{t \to \tau_\mathrm{m}}\ \langle H_\mathrm{B}(x(+t))\rangle_{(+)} - \langle H_\mathrm{B}(x(-t))\rangle_{(+)} \tag{9.14}$$

where the subscript $(+)$ implies an average value weighted by $P^{(+)}$. One may use the fact that propagating a system with all velocities flipped, $\mathbf{v}_i \to -\mathbf{v}_i$, is equivalent to a backward propagation in time to note that the transmission coefficient is equivalent to the net fraction of forward productive trajectories over the time interval $t \in [-\tau_\mathrm{m}, +\tau_\mathrm{m}]$ generated from the distribution $P^{(+)}$,

$$\kappa = \frac{N_{\mathrm{A}\to\mathrm{B}} - N_{\mathrm{B}\to\mathrm{A}}}{N_{\mathrm{A}\to\mathrm{B}} + N_{\mathrm{B}\to\mathrm{A}} + N_{\mathrm{A}\to\mathrm{A}} + N_{\mathrm{B}\to\mathrm{B}}} \tag{9.15}$$

where $N_{i\to j}$ is the number of activated trajectories observed to go from state i to state j.

9.3 The Kramers-Smoluchowski rate constant

A simple expression for the transition rate accounting for dissipative effects was derived by Kramers on the basis of the Smoluchowski diffusion equation [Kramers (1940)], which is valid if the dynamics of the particle trying to cross the barrier is described by Brownian dynamics. We consider a system with two stable states, A and B, that are separated by a large energy barrier and assume that a steady-state flux of probability is established from the well A to the well B by annihilating a particle as soon as it reaches the well B and immediately re-inserting it in the well A. Effectively, $P(x_\mathrm{B}) = 0$ at all time. By conservation of probability, the steady-state condition implies that the flux J is a constant. Based on the Smoluchowski diffusion equation, we have

$$\begin{aligned}
J &= -D\frac{\partial P}{\partial x} - \left(\frac{\partial W}{\partial x}\right)\frac{D}{k_\mathrm{B}T}P \\
&= -D\,\mathrm{e}^{-W/k_\mathrm{B}T}\frac{\partial}{\partial x}\left(\mathrm{e}^{+W/k_\mathrm{B}T}P(x)\right)
\end{aligned} \tag{9.16}$$

We then integrate the equation explicitly on both sides,

$$-\int_{x_A}^{x_B} \left(\frac{J \, e^{W(x)/k_B T}}{D(x)} \right) dx = \int_{x_A}^{x_B} \frac{\partial}{\partial x} \left(e^{+W(x)/k_B T} P(x) \right) dx$$

$$-J \int_{x_A}^{x_B} \left(\frac{e^{W(x)/k_B T}}{D(x)} \right) dx = \left(e^{+W(x)/k_B T} P(x) \right)\Big|_{x_1}^{x_2}$$

$$J \frac{e^{+W(x^\dagger)/k_B T}}{D(x^\dagger)} \left(\frac{2\pi k_B T}{|W''(x^\dagger)|} \right)^{1/2} = \left(e^{+W(x_A)/k_B T} P(x_A) - 0 \right) \qquad (9.17)$$

where we have used the fact that $P(x_B) = 0$ and approximated the potential $x^\dagger$ at the top of the barrier with a quadratic function,

$$W(x) \approx W(x^\dagger) - \frac{1}{2}|W''(x^\dagger)|(x - x^\dagger)^2 \qquad (9.18)$$

(note that $W''(x^\dagger) < 0$ at the top of the barrier). Here, $D(x^\dagger)$ is the diffusion constant at the barrier top, and $W''_{\max}$ is second derivative of the PMF evaluated at the top of the barrier top (note that $|W''(x^\dagger)|$ is positive). The steady-state probability in the well A is near the local equilibrium,

$$P(x) \approx \left(\frac{W''(x_A)}{2\pi k_B T} \right)^{1/2} e^{-\frac{1}{2}W''(x_A)(x-x_1)^2/k_B T} \qquad (9.19)$$

hence

$$P(x_A) \approx \left(\frac{W''(x_A)}{2\pi k_B T} \right)^{1/2} \qquad (9.20)$$

By virtue of the steady-state conditions, the flux J is equal to the Kramers-Smoluchowski transition rate for the process A → B,

$$k_{A \to B}^{(KS)} = \frac{D(x^\dagger)}{2\pi k_B T} (W''(x_A)|W''(x^\dagger)|)^{1/2} \, e^{-\Delta W^\dagger/k_B T} \qquad (9.21)$$

An essential aspect of this approximation, called "high friction limit," is that inertial dynamical effects are neglected, as indicated by the fact that the overall rate is independent of the mass.

Exercise: Derive the effective diffusion constant of a particle in a "rough potential.

Using the stationary flux from the Smoluchowski Eq. (9.16), it can be shown that the effective diffusion constant of a particle in a potential displaying a fine-scale spatial roughness can be estimated as the average one-dimensional resistance [Lifson and Jackson (1962); Zwanzig (1988); Golden *et al.* (1985)]

$$D_{\text{eff}} = \frac{k_B T}{\gamma} \left\langle e^{-W/k_B T} \right\rangle^{-1} \left\langle e^{+W/k_B T} \right\rangle^{-1} \tag{9.22}$$

where the bracket $\langle ... \rangle$ represent a spatial average over the diffusion space x, and γ is the static friction.

9.4 Advanced approximations of the transition rate constant

More advance approximations to the transmission coefficient can be derived by using Generalized Langevin Equation (GLE) introduced in section 7.7. The Grote-Hynes theory of barrier crossing expresses the transition rate as [Grote and Hynes (1980)],

$$\kappa = \frac{s}{\omega} \tag{9.23}$$

where $\omega = \sqrt{|W''(x^\dagger)|/m}$ is the frequency corresponding to the negative curvature of the PMF at the top of the barrier, s is the reactive frequency, obtained by solving the equation,

$$(\omega^2 - s^2) = \frac{s \widetilde{M}(s)}{m} \tag{9.24}$$

and $\widetilde{M}(s)$ represents the Laplace transform of the memory function,

$$\widetilde{M}(s) = \int_0^\infty M(t) e^{-st} dt \tag{9.25}$$

A graphical interpretation of Eq. (9.24) is depicted in Figure 9.3. If there is no dissipation, $\widetilde{M}(s) = 0$, then $s = \omega$, which yields $\kappa = 1$ based on Eq. (9.24) in accordance with the TST rate. The non-Markovian behavior and memory effects become negligible when the memory function $M(t)$ is large and decays rapidly compared to other timescales in the system, such as the frequency ω of the inverted energy barrier at the transition state. The Markovian regime is recovered if it is assumed that the memory

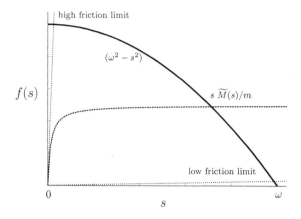

Fig. 9.3   Graphical representation of the Grote-Hynes Eq. (9.24). The solution requires two functions f of s, $\omega^2 - s^2$ (solid line) and $s\widetilde{M}(s)/m$ (dashed line) to cross at some point s between 0 and ω. In the low friction limit, the two curves cross at $s \approx \omega$ and the transmission coefficient $\kappa = s/\omega$ is close to 1. In the high friction limit, the two curves cross at a very small $s \approx m\omega^2/\gamma$, and the transmission coefficient κ is close to the Kramers-Smoluchowski result $\frac{m\omega}{\gamma}$. In the general case, the two curves may cross at any intermediate values between 0 and ω.

function decays extremely rapidly, as in the Langevin equation. Then, the dynamics is determined by the static friction constant, $\widetilde{M}(0) = \gamma$, and solving Eq. (9.24) amounts to finding the positive root of a simple quadratic equation, yielding the and the transmission coefficient,

$$\kappa = \sqrt{1 + \left(\frac{\gamma}{2m\omega}\right)^2} - \frac{\gamma}{2m\omega} \tag{9.26}$$

($\kappa = 1$ is recovered when $\gamma = 0$). This result was first obtained by Chandrasekar using Eq. (8.39). The high-friction Kramers-Smoluchowky transmission coefficient is obtained the limit that γ is very large,

$$\kappa = \frac{m\omega}{\gamma} \tag{9.27}$$

A simple alternative route to recover this result is to drop the s^2 in Eq. (9.24) arising from the Laplace transform of the inertial term $m\ddot{x}$ in the dynamics.

9.5   Brønsted analysis and Φ-values

Introducing small chemical perturbations (or site-directed mutations) into a system can be an interesting way to examine the relationship between the equilibrium constant and the transition rates. For example, such a method has been applied to examine the allosteric transition in the nicotinic acetylcholine receptor, an important transmembrane channel activated by the binding of acetylcholine [Grosman *et al.* (2000)].

Consider 2 states, A and B. The ratio of the equilibrium populations of state A and B is

$$\frac{P_A}{P_B} = \frac{e^{-W(x_A)/k_B T}}{e^{-W(x_B)/k_B T}} \tag{9.28}$$

the transition rate from A to B is

$$k_{A \to B} = f e^{-[W(x^\dagger) - W(x_A)]/k_B T} \tag{9.29}$$

where f is a frequency pre-factor, and the transition rate from B to A is

$$k_{B \to A} = f e^{-[W(x^\dagger) - W(x_B)]/k_B T} \tag{9.30}$$

For the sake of simplicity, it is assumed that the second derivatives of the wells at A and B, $W''(x_A)$ and $W''(x_B)$, are the same. Let us now consider the same system after a small perturbation "*" of $W(x)$. This could be, for example, a site-directed mutation has been introduced introduce in the system. Basically, the equilibrium constant and the rates are now altered slightly by the perturbation such that

$$\frac{P_A^*}{P_B^*} = \frac{e^{-W^*(x_A)/k_B T}}{e^{-W^*(x_B)/k_B T}} \tag{9.31}$$

the transition rate from A to B is

$$k_{A \to B}^* = f e^{-[W^*(x^\dagger) - W^*(x_A)]/k_B T} \tag{9.32}$$

and the transition rate from B to A is

$$k_{B \to A}^* = f e^{-[W^*(x^\dagger) - W^*(x_B)]/k_B T} \tag{9.33}$$

It is assumed that the influence of multiple perturbations can be represented as simple linear form,

$$W^*(x) = W(x) + C^*(x - x_A) \tag{9.34}$$

where C^* is some mutation-dependent number that could be either positive or negative. From this assumption, it is possible to extract information about the position of the transition state $x^\dagger$ relative to the two stable wells x_B and x_A from experimental measurements. We begin by defining the variable X,

$$\begin{aligned}
X &= -k_B T \ln\left[\frac{P_A^*/P_B^*}{P_A/P_B}\right] \\
&= [W^*(x_A) - W^*(x_B)] - [W(x_A) - W(x_B)] \\
&= C^*(x_B - x_A)
\end{aligned} \tag{9.35}$$

and the variable Y,

$$\begin{aligned}
Y &= -k_B T \ln\left[\frac{k_{A\to B}^*}{k_{A\to B}}\right] \\
&= [W^*(x^\dagger) - W^*(x_A)] - [W(x^\dagger) - W(x_A)] \\
&= C^*(x^\dagger - x_A)
\end{aligned} \tag{9.36}$$

Assuming that one has measured the effect of N mutations, each corresponding to different values of C_i^*, a plot of the N data points Y_i versus X_i will approximately lie on a straight line, with a slope of $\Phi = (x^\dagger - x_A)/(x_B - x_A)$. Here, the value of Φ represents the "position" of the transition state as a fraction of the "distance" between the state A and state B. For example, if Φ is much smaller than 0.5, this suggests that the transition state is more similar to state A than state B. Conversely, if Φ is much larger than 0.5, this suggests that the transition state is more similar to state B than state A.

9.6   Bimolecular association rate constant

So far we have only considered a "unimolecular" processes, i.e., occurring within a single molecule. The encounter of two molecules in solution requires a different treatment. The rate of formation of the complexes of A and B in solution can be described as

$$\frac{d}{dt}C_{AB} = k_{ass} C_A C_B \tag{9.37}$$

where k_{ass} is a bimolecular rate constant. For the sake of simplicity, let us consider a fixed molecule A surrounded by a dilute solution containing

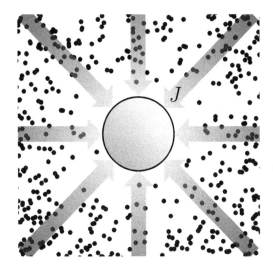

Fig. 9.4 Schematic representation of a system with one spherical receptor A of radius d fixed at the origin and surrounded by a solution of diffusing molecules B at concentration C_{B}.

molecules B. The molecule A is fixed at the origin of the reference coordinate system. The situation is illustrated in Figure 9.4.

Imagine now that the molecule B are made to vanish as soon as they reach the surface of molecule A. If we let this fictitious process carry on, a steady state will be established such that the concentration of B will be stationary. We assume that the system is spherically symmetric and that the ligands vanish when they cross $r = d$ (this is a big simplification, but it will get us to a useful expression). According to Fick's law, the net flux is

$$J = \frac{\text{Number of B molecules crossing a spherical surface S of radius } r}{\text{unit of time and unit of surface}}$$

$$= -D_{\mathrm{B}} \frac{\partial C(r)}{\partial r} \tag{9.38}$$

In 3 dimensions, the total number of incoming ligand molecules is the flux J times the area of the spherical surface $S = 4\pi r^2$,

$$I_{\mathrm{tot}} = JS$$

$$= \frac{\text{Number of B molecules crossing a spherical surface S of radius } r}{\text{unit of time}}$$

$$= -4\pi r^2 D_{\mathrm{B}} \frac{\partial C(r)}{\partial r} \tag{9.39}$$

We also have the following boundary conditions

$$C(r = \infty) = C_B$$

$$C(r = d) = 0 \tag{9.40}$$

When a stationary state is reached, then I_{tot} is a constant, thus one can write,

$$I_{tot} = 4\pi r^2 \left(-D_B \frac{\partial C}{\partial r} \right)$$

$$\int_d^\infty \left(\frac{I_{tot}}{4\pi r^2 D_B} \right) dr = -\int_d^\infty dC$$

$$-\frac{I_{tot}}{4\pi D_B r} \Big|_d^\infty = C_B$$

$$I_{tot} = 4\pi \, d \, D_B \, C_B \tag{9.41}$$

This is the rate for molecules B diffusing and colliding with a single fixed spherical molecule A. If there is a certain concentration of molecules A in solution, then the total number of moles of bound complexes formed per unit of time per liter for the process A+B→AB is $C_A I_{tot}$,

$$\frac{d}{dt} C_{AB} = k_{ass} \, C_A \, C_B \tag{9.42}$$

and the bimolecular association rate constant is

$$k_{ass} = 4\pi \, d \, (D_A + D_B) \tag{9.43}$$

where D_A and D_B are the diffusion constants of the molecule A and B. If one of the two molecules is much smaller than the other then its diffusion constant will typically dominate the bimolecular association rate constant.

It is also possible to restart from Eq. (9.41) but instead integrate the left and right sides from r to ∞ to determine the spatial concentration profile $C(r)$ under the same stationary conditions,

$$C(r) = C_B \left(1 - \frac{d}{r} \right) \tag{9.44}$$

The Figure 9.5 shows that the concentration of molecules B drops very rapidly near the surface of the central molecule A.

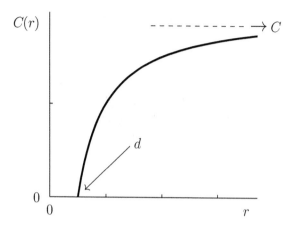

Fig. 9.5 Concentration profile of the molecules B normalized by C_B around the molecule A as a function of the distance r/d.

Exercise: Bimolecular association rate in the presence of a PMF.
Use the Smoluchowski diffusion equation to show that

$$k_{ass} = 4\pi(D_A + D_B)\left(\int_\infty^d \frac{e^{+W(r)/k_B T}}{r^2}\,dr\right)^{-1} \tag{9.45}$$

if there is a radial PMF $W(r)$ between the particles A and B.

It is also of interest to introduce the possibility of dissociation in a more complete description of the kinetics,

$$\frac{d}{dt}C_{AB} = k_{ass}\,C_A\,C_B - k_{diss}\,C_{AB} \tag{9.46}$$

where k_{diss} is the dissociation rate constant. Because dissociation is effectively a unimolecular process, we can lean on the calculation of transition rates discussed in Sections 9.1 to 9.4. When the system is at equilibrium, the time derivative is equal to zero,

$$0 = k_{ass}\,C_A\,C_B - k_{diss}\,C_{AB} \tag{9.47}$$

which yields,

$$C_{AB} = \frac{k_{ass}}{k_{diss}}\,C_A\,C_B \tag{9.48}$$

This shows that the equilibrium binding constant as described in Chapter 5 is given by

$$K_b = \frac{k_{ass}}{k_{diss}} \tag{9.49}$$

An interesting exercise is relate, for example, the Kramers-Smoluchowski expressions for the association and dissociation rates Eqs. (9.21) and (9.45) to the equilibrium binding constant from Eq. (5.15).

Chapter 10

Dynamics of discrete state models

In Chapter 9, we saw that the long timescale transitions between two stable states take the form of a simple rate dependence. This simplified picture can be generalized to represent the dynamical evolution of a complex system in terms of kinetic models with multiple discrete states. When the transitions between the different states do not depend on the past history, the system is then said to evolve dynamically with no memory. Mathematically, such a kinetic model is called a discrete-state continuous-time Markov chain (named after the Russian mathematician Andrey Andreyevich Markov, 1856–1922). A discrete-state continuous-time Markov chain is a stochastic model in which the probability of the transition from state i to state j depends only on the current state i, and not the previous history of the system. A typical Markov chain is depicted in Figure 10.1. The dynamics of this type of model is governed by the state-to-state transition rates, which are the input parameters. While this simplified representation may look somewhat artificial, it is a physically valid approximation when long-timescale properties are dominated by the rare transitions between a set of long-living metastable states. Furthermore, it is important to recall that the transition rates arise from the well-defined statistical mechanical features of detailed atomic models (see Chapter 9). Therefore, kinetic models with discrete states may be constructed in such a way that remains faithfully representative of the microscopic system of interest with respect to long-timescale properties.

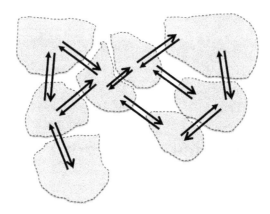

Fig. 10.1   Illustration of a Markov chain with discrete states. The arrows between the states represent transition rates (number of transitions per unit of time). The Markov chain is said to be irreducible if all the states are accessible during a single unbroken trajectory.

10.1   Simple kinetic model with two states

The simplest kinetic model comprises only transitions between two stable states,

$$A \underset{k_{B \to A}}{\overset{k_{A \to B}}{\rightleftharpoons}} B$$

Let P_A^{eq} and P_B^{eq} be the equilibrium probability of states A and B, respectively. We then have the ratio,

$$\frac{P_B^{eq}}{P_A^{eq}} = \frac{\int_{x^{\ddagger}}^{\infty} e^{-W(x)/k_B T} dx}{\int_{-\infty}^{x^{\ddagger}} e^{-W(x)/k_B T} dx} \tag{10.1}$$

which can be combined with the normalization condition, $P_A^{eq} + P_B^{eq} = 1$, to constrain the equilibrium properties of the model. It is customary to denote the equilibrium probability of the state as $P_i^{eq} = \pi_i$.

The dynamics of the two-state system is incorporated into the transition rates $k_{A \to B}$ and $k_{B \to A}$, which represent the probability to make a transition to state B while being in state A per unit time, and vice versa. These transition rates can, in principle, be calculated rigorously as a function of the microscopic features of the system (see Section 9.2 in Chapter 9). The dynamic evolution of the time-dependent probabilities can be derived in the following manner. Let us express the probability that the system is in state A at the time $t + \Delta t$ as,

$$P_A(t + \Delta t) = P_A(t) \times \text{Prob(no transition from A to B during } \Delta t)$$
$$+ P_B(t) \times \text{Prob(transition from B to A during } \Delta t) \quad (10.2)$$

The probability that there is no transition from A to B during the time interval Δt is $(1 - k_{A \to B} \Delta t)$, while the probability that there is a transition from B to A during the time interval Δt is $k_{B \to A} \Delta t$. It follows that

$$P_A(t + \Delta t) = P_A(t) \times (1 - k_{A \to B} \Delta t)$$
$$+ P_B(t) \times k_{B \to A} \Delta t \quad (10.3)$$

which leads to

$$\frac{P_A(t + \Delta t) - P_A(t)}{\Delta t} = -P_A(t) k_{A \to B} + P_B(t) k_{B \to A} \quad (10.4)$$

A similar transformation may be carried out for the time-dependent probability $P_B(t)$. Taking the limit of Δt approaching zero, it follows that the time-dependent probabilities evolve according to the differential equations,

$$\dot{P}_A(t) = -k_{A \to B} P_A(t) + k_{B \to A} P_B(t)$$
$$\dot{P}_B(t) = k_{A \to B} P_A(t) - k_{B \to A} P_B(t) \quad (10.5)$$

The equilibrium solution is expected to be independent of time, with $dP_A(t)/dt = 0$ and $dP_B(t)/dt = 0$. Imposing this condition to Eqs. (10.5) and (10.5) leads to the relation,

$$P_A^{eq} k_{A \to B} = P_B^{eq} k_{B \to A} \quad (10.6)$$

which implies that the total net flux from state A to state B must be equal to the total net flux from state B to state A. This constraint, linking the transition rates and the equilibrium probabilities of the model, is called microscopic detailed balance. It follows that the time-independent equilibrium probability of the state A and B is

$$P_A^{eq} = \frac{k_{B \to A}}{k_{A \to B} + k_{B \to A}} \quad (10.7)$$

and

$$P_{\mathrm{B}}^{\mathrm{eq}} = \frac{k_{\mathrm{A}\to\mathrm{B}}}{k_{\mathrm{A}\to\mathrm{B}} + k_{\mathrm{B}\to\mathrm{A}}} \qquad (10.8)$$

respectively. It can be verified by substitution that a general solution of Eqs. (10.5) and (10.5) is,

$$P_{\mathrm{A}}(t) = P_{\mathrm{A}}^{\mathrm{eq}} + \left(P_{\mathrm{A}}(0) - P_{\mathrm{A}}^{\mathrm{eq}}\right) e^{-t/\tau}$$

$$P_{\mathrm{B}}(t) = P_{\mathrm{B}}^{\mathrm{eq}} + \left(P_{\mathrm{B}}(0) - P_{\mathrm{B}}^{\mathrm{eq}}\right) e^{-t/\tau} \qquad (10.9)$$

where $\tau = (k_{\mathrm{A}\to\mathrm{B}} + k_{\mathrm{B}\to\mathrm{A}})^{-1}$ is the overall relaxation time of the two-state system. It is frequently more convenient to work with the conditional probabilities, $P_{ij}(t) = \mathrm{Prob}[\mathrm{state}(t) = j | \mathrm{state}(t = 0) = i]$, which can be determined from the general solution.

It is also useful to consider the probability of the system staying in a given state for a time t. For example, the probability of staying in state A for a time t can be calculated by considering Eqs. (10.5) and setting the transition rate to return from state B to zero, $k_{\mathrm{B}\to\mathrm{A}} = 0$,

$$\frac{dP_{\mathrm{A}}(t)}{dt} = -k_{\mathrm{A}\to\mathrm{B}} \, P_{\mathrm{A}}(t) \qquad (10.10)$$

In other words, state B is treated as an absorbing state (no possibility of making a transition out of the state B). The solution to Eq. (10.10) is,

$$P_{\mathrm{A}}(t) = e^{-k_{\mathrm{A}\to\mathrm{B}}t} \qquad (10.11)$$

This is the probability to be found in state A after a time t (also called the survival probability). Likewise, the probability density of staying in A for a time t and then making a transition to state B within a time interval dt is, $p_{\mathrm{A}}(t) = -dP_{\mathrm{A}}(t)/dt$,

$$p_{\mathrm{A}}(t) \, dt = e^{-k_{\mathrm{A}\to\mathrm{B}}t} \left(k_{\mathrm{A}\to\mathrm{B}} \, dt\right) \qquad (10.12)$$

A similar expressions can be derived for state B. The simple two-state model allows us to illustrate several aspects of Markov chains. In the following, we will further elaborate on the mathematical structure of kinetic models with a larger number of states.

10.2   Discrete state continuous-time Markov chain

These ideas may be generalized to Markov chain with M states. They provide a powerful framework to construct models of complex biomolecular systems. Let $P_{ij}(t)$ be the probability that the system starts in state i at time $t = 0$ and reaches state j at time t, with $t > 0$. The probability $P_{ij}(t)$ must obey the following set of conditions,

$$P_{ij}(t) > 0$$

$$\sum_{j=1}^{M} P_{ij}(t) = 1$$

$$\lim_{t \to 0} P_{ij}(t) = \delta_{ij} \tag{10.13}$$

To obtain the dynamical evolution of $P_{ij}(t)$, we express the probability that the system is in state j at time $t + \Delta t$, $P_{ij}(t + \Delta t)$, as the probability that the system is in state j at time t, $P_{ij}(t)$, times the probability that there is no transition from the state j to any other state s during the interval Δt, plus the total incoming probability fluxes to the state j summed over all other states s,

$$P_{ij}(t + \Delta t) = P_{ij}(t) \left(1 - \sum_{s \neq j}^{M} k_{js} \Delta t \right) + \left(\sum_{s \neq j}^{M} P_{is}(t) k_{sj} \Delta t \right) \tag{10.14}$$

where M is the total number of states. From this expression, we can write:

$$P_{ij}(t + \Delta t) - P_{ij}(t) = -P_{ij}(t) \sum_{s \neq j}^{M} k_{js} \Delta t + \sum_{s \neq j}^{M} P_{is}(t) k_{sj} \Delta t$$

$$\frac{P_{ij}(t + \Delta t) - P_{ij}(t)}{\Delta t} = -P_{ij}(t) \sum_{s \neq j}^{M} k_{js} + \sum_{s \neq j}^{M} P_{is}(t) k_{sj} \tag{10.15}$$

taking the limit of Δt approaching zero leads to:

$$\dot{P}_{ij}(t) = -P_{ij}(t) \sum_{s \neq j}^{M} k_{js} + \sum_{s \neq j}^{M} P_{is}(t) k_{sj} \tag{10.16}$$

This is called the master equation, which may be written as,

$$\dot{P}_{ij}(t) = \sum_{s=1}^{M} P_{is}(t) Q_{sj} \tag{10.17}$$

or in matrix form, $\dot{\mathbf{P}} = \mathbf{PQ}$, where the elements of the matrix $\mathbf{Q}$ are defined as

$$\mathbf{Q} = \begin{pmatrix} -\sum_{s \neq 1} k_{1s} & k_{12} & k_{13} & \cdots \\ k_{21} & -\sum_{s \neq 2} k_{2s} & k_{23} & \cdots \\ k_{31} & k_{32} & -\sum_{s \neq 3} k_{3s} & \cdots \\ \cdots & \cdots & \cdots & \cdots \end{pmatrix} \qquad (10.18)$$

The diagonal term of the matrix Q_{ii} corresponds to the negative sum of all the outgoing transition rates from the state i.

To obtain a time-independent equation for the equilibrium solution, it is tempting to simply set the derivative $\dot{P}_{ij}(t) = 0$. However, this condition may not be sufficient to obtain a physically acceptable model in thermodynamic equilibrium. For instance, even if the probabilities P_i are independent of time, the probability could flow among a subset of states, for example, $i \to j \to k \to i$, in a manner that is inconsistent with a true thermodynamic equilibrium. An example of a Markov chain in which the probability of the three states could remain independent of time while sustaining a loop of probability current is depicted in Figure 10.2. This type of behavior is physically possible, but only when the system is coupled

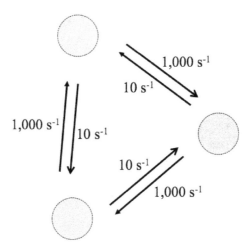

Fig. 10.2   Illustration of a probability loop transition while the probability of the states remains independent of time. By default, the probability of the three states will be independent of time if they are assumed to be equal (1/3).

to an external source of energy, such as a concentration gradient across a membrane, or a high concentration of ATP compared to ADP, for example (this will be discussed in Chapter 12). Such systematic flux within a system cannot be sustained under true equilibrium conditions. To prevent this issue from occurring under equilibrium conditions, Markov models are typically further constrained through state-to-state microscopic detailed balance,

$$P_i^{eq} k_{ij} = P_j^{eq} k_{ji} \qquad (10.19)$$

which enforces the condition that the total flux from state i to state j be equal to the total flux from state j to state i. Eq. (10.19) must be satisfied for all pairs of state i and j. Satisfying state-to-state microscopic detailed balance Eq. (10.19) for all pairs of state i and j is sufficient to prohibit the existence of any loops of probability current that are inconsistent with thermodynamic equilibrium. This provides a strong constraint to insure that the underlying structure of the Markov chain is physically sound. It is easy to show that the master equation conserves total probability,

$$1 = \sum_{j=1}^{M} P_{ij}(t)$$

$$0 = \sum_{j=1}^{M} \dot{P}_{ij}(t)$$

$$0 = \sum_{j=1}^{M} \sum_{s=1}^{M} P_{is}(t) Q_{sj} \qquad (10.20)$$

which is verified because $\sum_{j=1}^{M} Q_{sj} = 0$ by design.

The solution to the master equation is an exponential of matrix, which can be formally expressed as,

$$\mathbf{P}(t) = e^{\mathbf{Q}t} = \mathbf{I} + \mathbf{Q}t + \frac{1}{2}\mathbf{Q}^2 t^2 + \cdots \qquad (10.21)$$

($P_{ij}(t)$ is equal to the ij matrix element $[e^{\mathbf{Q}t}]_{ij}$). The formal solution makes it clear that the time-dependent probability satisfies the Chapman–Kolmogorov equation,

$$e^{\mathbf{Q}(t_1+t_2)} = e^{\mathbf{Q}t_1} e^{\mathbf{Q}t_2} \qquad (10.22)$$

or more specifically,

$$P_{ij}(t_1 + t_2) = \sum_s P_{is}(t_1)P_{sj}(t_2) \tag{10.23}$$

The solution can be expressed via a spectral decomposition,

$$e^{\mathbf{Q}t} = \mathbf{U}^{-1} \begin{pmatrix} e^{\lambda_1 t} & & 0 \\ & \ddots & \\ 0 & & e^{\lambda_M t} \end{pmatrix} \mathbf{U} \tag{10.24}$$

where $\mathbf{U}$ is the square $N \times N$ matrix whose i-th line is the eigenvector $\mathbf{u}_i$ of $\mathbf{Q}$ with associated eigenvalue λ_i,

$$(\mathbf{u}_i)^\top \cdot \mathbf{Q} = \lambda_i (\mathbf{u}_i)^\top \tag{10.25}$$

The above development shows that the probability $P_{ij}(t)$ follows a multiexponential relaxation decay. In this regard, three important and general properties about the matrix $\mathbf{Q}$ must be established. First, while the matrix $\mathbf{Q}$ is not symmetric, it can be shown that its eigenvalues are real by transforming $\mathbf{Q}$ into a symmetrical matrix $\mathbf{M}$ via the following operation:

$$M_{ij} = Q_{ij} \left(\frac{P_i^{eq}}{P_j^{eq}} \right)^{1/2} \tag{10.26}$$

and

$$M_{ij} = M_{ji}$$

$$Q_{ij} \left(\frac{P_i^{eq}}{P_j^{eq}} \right)^{1/2} = Q_{ji} \left(\frac{P_j^{eq}}{P_i^{eq}} \right)^{1/2}$$

$$Q_{ij} P_i^{eq} = Q_{ji} P_j^{eq} \tag{10.27}$$

is satisfied via the detailed-balance condition. The matrix $\mathbf{Q}$ and $\mathbf{M}$ have the same eigenvalues. Because $\mathbf{M}$ is symmetric, the eigenvalues must be real. Second, at least one eigenvalue must be equal to zero because the sum of columns is zero for all the lines of the matrix. In fact, as prescribed by the microscopic detailed balance conditions, $P_j^{eq} Q_{ji} = P_i^{eq} Q_{ij}$, it is easy to show that the left eigenvector with associated eigenvalue equal to zero is the equilibrium probability,

$$\sum_i P_i^{\text{eq}} Q_{ij} = P_j^{\text{eq}} Q_{jj} + \sum_{i \neq j} P_i^{\text{eq}} Q_{ij}$$

$$= P_j^{\text{eq}} \left(-\sum_{i \neq j} Q_{ji} \right) + \sum_{i \neq j} P_i^{\text{eq}} Q_{ij}$$

$$= \sum_{i \neq j} -P_j^{\text{eq}} Q_{ji} + P_i^{\text{eq}} Q_{ij}$$

$$= \sum_{i \neq j} 0$$

$$= 0 \, P_j^{\text{eq}} \tag{10.28}$$

Third, while one eigenvalue of $\mathbf{Q}$ associated with the equilibrium vector is equal to zero, all the remaining eigenvalues of $\mathbf{Q}$ are negative. This can be demonstrated using a special case of Gershgorin's theorem, stating that the eigenvalues of the matrix $\mathbf{Q}$ must obey the inequality,

$$\lambda_i - Q_{ii} \leq \sum_{j \neq i} Q_{ij}$$

$$\lambda_i \leq Q_{ii} + \sum_{j \neq i} Q_{ij}$$

$$\lambda_i \leq 0 \tag{10.29}$$

(Gershgorin's theorem is more general and states that the eigenvalues must lie within the N circles of radius $R_i = \sum_{j \neq i} |Q_{ij}|$ and centered at Q_{ii} in the complex plane: $|\lambda_i - Q_{ii}| \leq R_i$.) Therefore, all the eigenvectors associated with $\lambda_i < 0$ decay to zero in the limit of $t \to \infty$, and the system relaxes to the equilibrium probability (the eigenvector with $\lambda_1 = 0$).

10.3 Probability expressed as a sum over all possible paths

Ultimately, we will be interested in simulating such Markov models by generating random paths visiting different states as function of time. Whether one can demonstrate that the sum over all possible paths is equivalent to the formal solution of the master equation is an important question,

$$P_{ij}(t) = \sum_{\substack{\text{All paths of length } t \\ \text{starting in } i \text{ and ending in } j}} \text{Probability}\{\text{path}\} \qquad (10.30)$$

To begin the analysis, let us first consider a given path comprising n transitions visiting a sequence of states starting in i and ending in j, $\{i, s_1, \ldots, s_{n-1}, j\}$, with a set of n temporary stops (sojourns) of length $\{t_0, t_1, \ldots, t_{n-1}, t_n\}$. The question is whether we are able to get the total probability to find the system in state j at time t, $P_{ij}(t)$, by summing over all possible paths comprising any number of transitions n starting in i and ending in j, $\{i, s_1, \ldots, s_{n-1}, j\}$, and integrate over possible combination of sojourns $\{t_0, t_1, \ldots, t_{n-1}, t_n\}$ under the constraint that $\sum_n t_n = t$. We need to sum over all $s_1 \neq i$, all $s_2 \neq s_3$, and so on, and integrate over all possible t_0, t_1, and t_n, such that $\sum_n t_n = t$. For convenience, let us define the matrix $\mathbf{D}$ such that it is equal to only the diagonal terms of the matrix $\mathbf{Q}$, and the define the matrix $\mathbf{R}$ for the remaining non-diagonal terms. By definition, $\mathbf{Q} = \mathbf{D} + \mathbf{R}$. The probability of a given path comprising n transitions, with a set of $n+1$ sojourns of length $\{t_0, t_1, t_2, \ldots, t_n\}$ in all possible suite of states is $e^{\mathbf{D}t_0}\mathbf{R}e^{\mathbf{D}t_1}\mathbf{R}\ldots e^{\mathbf{D}t_n}\, dt_0\, dt_1 \ldots dt_n$. The total probability to find the system in state j at time t is the ij element of the matrix,

$$e^{\mathbf{Q}t} = \sum_{n\geq 0} \int_0^\infty dt_0 \cdots \int_0^\infty dt_n\, e^{\mathbf{D}t_0}\mathbf{R}e^{\mathbf{D}t_1}\mathbf{R}\ldots e^{\mathbf{D}t_n}\, \delta\left(\sum_{\alpha=0}^n t_\alpha - t\right)$$

$$(10.31)$$

We write the delta function as,

$$\delta\left(\sum_{\alpha=0}^n t_\alpha - t\right) = \frac{1}{2\pi}\int_{-\infty}^\infty du\, e^{iu(t_0 + t_1 \cdots + t_n - t)} \qquad (10.32)$$

The Fourier–Laplace transform of $e^{\mathbf{D}t}$ is

$$\int_0^\infty dt'\, e^{\mathbf{D}t'}\, e^{iut'} = \int_0^\infty dt'\, e^{(\mathbf{D}+iu\mathbf{I})t'}$$

$$= -(\mathbf{D} + iu\mathbf{I})^{-1} \qquad (10.33)$$

The integral is well-defined, as all the terms in the diagonal matrix $\mathbf{D}$ are negative. So, the expression becomes:

$$e^{\mathbf{Q}t} = \sum_{n\geq 0} -\frac{1}{2\pi}\int_{-\infty}^\infty du\, e^{-iut}\, (\mathbf{D} + iu\mathbf{I})^{-1}\left[-\mathbf{R}(\mathbf{D}+iu\mathbf{I})^{-1}\right]^n \qquad (10.34)$$

We can use the identity for a geometric series,

$$\sum_{n \geq 0} \mathbf{X}^n = (\mathbf{I} - \mathbf{X})^{-1} \tag{10.35}$$

with the matrix $\mathbf{X} = -\mathbf{R}(\mathbf{D} + iu\mathbf{I})^{-1}$. This infinite sum then becomes,

$$\sum_{n \geq 0} \left[-\mathbf{R}(\mathbf{D} + iu\mathbf{I})^{-1} \right]^n = \left(\mathbf{I} + \left[\mathbf{R}(\mathbf{D} + iu\mathbf{I})^{-1}\right]\right)^{-1} \tag{10.36}$$

Substituting this expression in the sum leads to,

$$e^{\mathbf{Q}t} = -\frac{1}{2\pi} \int_{-\infty}^{\infty} du \, e^{-iut} \, (\mathbf{D} + iu\mathbf{I})^{-1} \left(\mathbf{I} + \left[\mathbf{R}(\mathbf{D} + iu\mathbf{I})^{-1}\right]\right)^{-1} \tag{10.37}$$

and using the fact that for invertible matrices,

$$(\mathbf{AB})^{-1}(\mathbf{AB}) = \mathbf{I}$$
$$(\mathbf{AB})^{-1}\mathbf{A} = \mathbf{B}^{-1}$$
$$(\mathbf{AB})^{-1} = \mathbf{B}^{-1}\mathbf{A}^{-1} \tag{10.38}$$

the expression can be simplified as,

$$e^{\mathbf{Q}t} = -\frac{1}{2\pi} \int_{-\infty}^{\infty} du \, e^{-iut} \left[\left(\mathbf{I} + \mathbf{R}(\mathbf{D} + iu\mathbf{I})^{-1}\right)(\mathbf{D} + iu\mathbf{I})\right]^{-1}$$

$$e^{\mathbf{Q}t} = -\frac{1}{2\pi} \int_{-\infty}^{\infty} du \, e^{-iut} \left(\mathbf{D} + \mathbf{R} + iu\mathbf{I}\right)^{-1}$$

$$e^{\mathbf{Q}t} = -\frac{1}{2\pi} \int_{-\infty}^{\infty} du \, e^{-iut} \left(\mathbf{Q} + iu\mathbf{I}\right)^{-1} \tag{10.39}$$

We can recognize that the term $(\mathbf{Q} + iu\mathbf{I})^{-1}$ on the r.h.s. is the Fourier–Laplace transform of $e^{\mathbf{Q}t}$. This demonstrates that the time-dependent probability of a discrete-state continuous-time Markov chain can indeed be expressed as a weighted sum over all possible paths, as we had conjectured. We will see in Section 11.8 of Chapter 11 that this identity will be critical in practical simulations of Markov chains [Gillespie (1976)].

10.4 Markov chains with discrete time

Markov chains with discrete time are widely used to analyze molecular dynamics (MD) simulation data [Bowman *et al.* (2014)]. Starting from the master equation, it is possible to construct a Markov chain with the discrete coarse-grained propagation time τ (called the lag-time),

$$\mathbf{T}(\tau) = e^{\mathbf{Q}\tau} \tag{10.40}$$

where $\mathbf{T}(\tau)$ is the transition matrix for the lag-time τ. The transition matrix can be represented in diagonal form:

$$\mathbf{T}(\tau) = \mathbf{U}^{-1} \begin{pmatrix} e^{\lambda_1 \tau} & & 0 \\ & \ddots & \\ 0 & & e^{\lambda_n \tau} \end{pmatrix} \mathbf{U}$$

$$= \mathbf{U}^{-1} \begin{pmatrix} \Lambda_1(\tau) & & 0 \\ & \ddots & \\ 0 & & \Lambda_N(\tau) \end{pmatrix} \mathbf{U} \tag{10.41}$$

Effectively, the eigenvalues $\Lambda_i(\tau)$ of the transition matrix $\mathbf{T}(\tau)$ are related to the eigenvalues λ_i of the matrix $\mathbf{Q}$, with $\Lambda_i(\tau) = e^{\lambda_i \tau}$. Thus, the eigenvalue of the transition matrix $\mathbf{T}(\tau)$ associated to the equilibrium vector is equal to 1 because the eigenvalue of the transition matrix $\mathbf{Q}$ associated to the equilibrium vector is equal to zero. Therefore, propagation of the equilibrium eigenvector π_i is expected to maintain equilibrium,

$$\sum_i \pi_i T_{ij} = \pi_j \tag{10.42}$$

or in matrix notation $\pi \mathbf{T}(\tau) = \pi$. The other eigenvalues $\Lambda_i(\tau)$ are all smaller than 1 (because $\lambda_i \leq 0$). Propagation of the Markov chain for n steps yields,

$$\mathbf{T}(n\tau) = (\mathbf{T}(\tau))^n$$

$$= \mathbf{U}^{-1} \begin{pmatrix} \Lambda_1(\tau)^n & & 0 \\ & \ddots & \\ 0 & & \Lambda_N(\tau)^n \end{pmatrix} \mathbf{U} \tag{10.43}$$

In the limit of $n \to \infty$, the eigenvectors associated with $\Lambda_i(\tau) < 1$ decay to zero and the system relaxes to the equilibrium probability (the eigenvector with $\Lambda_1(\tau) = 1$). The largest eigenvalue that differs from 1 governs the characteristic relaxation time. The stationary distribution is the equilibrium probability π, which is the left eigenvector of the matrix $\mathbf{T}(\tau)$. This analysis also shows that the eigenvalues of the transition matrix $\mathbf{T}(n\tau)$ with the lag-time $n\tau$ are related to the eigenvalues of the transition matrix $\mathbf{T}(\tau)$ with the lag-time τ,

$$\Lambda_i(n\tau) = \Lambda_i(\tau)^n \tag{10.44}$$

Thus, the relation $\ln[\Lambda_i(n\tau)]/n = \ln[\Lambda_i(\tau)]$ must be satisfied for a valid discrete-time Markov chain. This condition is utilized to examine the validity of Markov models constructed from MD data. The Markov transition matrix $\mathbf{T}(\tau)$ is constructed for different values of τ, until the relation is satisfied.

A quantity of great interest to help understand the character of the landscape of states separating a "reactant" state A and the "product" state B is the probability q_i for starting a random trajectory in the state i and reaching B before returning to A. The probability q_i is called the forward committor function. By design, $q_A = 0$ and $q_B = 1$, because if the trajectory starts in A, then the probability to reach B is zero, and if the trajectory starts in B, then the probability to reach B is 1. The general form of q_i can be expressed as a sum over all possible paths starting in state $i \neq A$ and subsequently visiting a series of states other than A or B, until making a final transition to state B,

$$q_i = \mathbf{T}_{iB} + \sum_{j \neq A,B} \mathbf{T}_{ij}\mathbf{T}_{jB} + \sum_{\substack{j \neq A,B \\ k \neq A,B}} \mathbf{T}_{ij}\mathbf{T}_{jk}\mathbf{T}_{kB} + \sum_{\substack{j \neq A,B \\ k \neq A,B \\ l \neq A,B}} \mathbf{T}_{ij}\mathbf{T}_{jk}\mathbf{T}_{kl}\mathbf{T}_{lB} + \cdots$$

$$= \mathbf{T}_{iB} + \sum_{j \neq A,B} \mathbf{T}_{ij} \left[\mathbf{T}_{jB} + \sum_{k \neq A,B} \mathbf{T}_{jk}\mathbf{T}_{kB} + \sum_{\substack{k \neq A,B \\ l \neq A,B}} \mathbf{T}_{kl}\mathbf{T}_{lB} + \cdots \right]$$

$$= \mathbf{T}_{iB} + \sum_{j \neq A,B} \mathbf{T}_{ij}\, q_j$$

$$= \mathbf{T}_{iA}\, q_A + \mathbf{T}_{iB}\, q_B + \sum_{j \neq A,B} \mathbf{T}_{ij}\, q_j$$

$$= \sum_{j} \mathbf{T}_{ij}\, q_j \tag{10.45}$$

with the constraint that $q_A = 0$ and $q_B = 1$. This relation can also be written in matrix form as,

$$\mathbf{q} = \mathbf{T}\mathbf{q} \tag{10.46}$$

which shows that the forward committor is like a right-eigenvector to the state-to-state transition matrix. But this relation is valid only for states other than A and B due to the constraints $q_A = 0$ and $q_B = 1$.

Chapter 11

Stochastic simulations

Many of the effective dynamical models that were introduced incorporate elements of stochasticity and randomness. For example, the random walk is a process that evolves through discrete steps in unpredictable directions, the dynamics from the Langevin equation obeys Newton's equation of motion but with a Gaussian random force, and the dynamics of a kinetic Markov model is a stochastic trajectory that comprises periods of staying in a given state for a random period of time followed by a discrete jump to another state. To simulate these formal models on a computer requires random numbers with specific probability distributions. In everyday life, familiar mechanical devices are used to produce randomness (Figure 11.1). For example, throwing a coin yielding head or tail can be used to generate random numbers with probability one-half. Or throwing a dice with six faces can be used to generate random numbers between 1 and 6. One may combine various combinations of the dice's faces together to generate random numbers with a probability of $1/6$, $2/6$, $3/6$, $4/6$, and $5/6$. The latter example shows that it is possible to manipulate the outcome from a given device to generate random numbers with different probabilities. Nevertheless, such simple mechanical devices have obvious limitations when a very large number of repetitive steps must be taken. There are some electronic devices that appear to genuinely be random (e.g., involving particle decay), which could be linked to a computer to simulate stochastic processes. But commonly, it is more convenient to use lists of "pseudo-random" numbers that are generated via some deterministic algorithms. One advantage of pseudo-random numbers is that one can control and repeat the suite of

Fig. 11.1 Randomness in everyday life. A classic dice with six faces (left). Flipping a coin to generate a random outcome with a probability of one half (right).

numbers whenever desired, which is useful for debugging and analyzing code performance.

11.1 Pseudo-random number generators

One of the earliest pseudo-random number generators was designed at IBM in the 1960s [Lewis *et al.* (1969)]. While not flawless, this simple algorithm provides a useful illustrative example. It generates pseudo-random numbers R that are uniformly distributed between 0 and 1 ($R \in [0, 1]$). It is based on the simple expression,

$$R = \frac{\mathrm{Mod}(\overbrace{M}^{16807} \cdot \overbrace{\text{iseed}}^{\text{input}}, \overbrace{\text{divi}}^{2,147,483,647})}{\underbrace{\text{denom}}_{2,147,483,711}} \tag{11.1}$$

where iseed is an integer number given as input by the user to initiate the sequence that is replaced at each new cycle by:

$$\text{new iseed} = \mathrm{Mod}(M \cdot \text{iseed}, \text{div}) \tag{11.2}$$

The operation $\mathrm{Mod}(n, m)$ for two positive integers n and m finds the remainder after division of n by m (e.g., $\mathrm{Mod}(79, 17) = 11$). The number "iseed" is an initial integer that must be provided by the user. The number used for "divi" (2,147,483,647) is the 8th Mersenne prime number, equal to 2^{31}-1 (discovered by Marin Mersenne, 1588–1648). It remained the largest known prime number until 1867. The practical steps of the algorithm proceed as follows. As an illustration, let us follow three cycles of the pseudo-random number generator based on Eq. (11.1) starting with a iseed set to 314159:

Cycle 1:
iseed	314159
$M \cdot$iseed	5280070313
$\mathrm{Mod}(M \cdot \mathrm{iseed}, \mathrm{div})$	985103019
$R = \mathrm{Mod}()/\mathrm{denom}$	0.45872

Cycle 2:
iseed	985103019
$M \cdot$iseed	16556626440333
$\mathrm{Mod}(M \cdot \mathrm{iseed}, \mathrm{div})$	1675005610
$R = \mathrm{Mod}()/\mathrm{denom}$	0.77999

Cycle 3:
iseed	1675005610
$M \cdot$iseed	28151819287270
$\mathrm{Mod}(M \cdot \mathrm{iseed}, \mathrm{div})$	456158747
$R = \mathrm{Mod}()/\mathrm{denom}$	0.21242

The algorithm produces a sequence of numbers R, which are uniformly distributed within the interval $[0, 1]$, and which appear to be essentially uncorrelated with one another. Regarding this last point, it is more accurate to state that the numbers do not display any immediate correlation. In fact, the pseudo-random numbers generated via Eq. (11.1) can display several pathologies with disastrous consequences for stochastic simulations. For example, there can be hidden correlations such that the generated numbers are not truly independent. An even worse problem is that of "loop recurrence, which occurs when the same sequence of numbers keep on being repeated in the same order. Typically, the length of the recurring loop depends on the seed used to initiate the generator. Over the years, several of these issues have become better understood, and more sophisticated pseudo-random number generators were developed. Users should always be aware of the imperfections in pseudo-random number generator algorithms that are used in extensive computations.

This type of algorithm is sometimes referred to as a "uniform unit-interval random number generator." The utilization of uniformly distributed pseudo-random numbers in simple practical calculations may be illustrated with the following example. We can use R to calculate the value

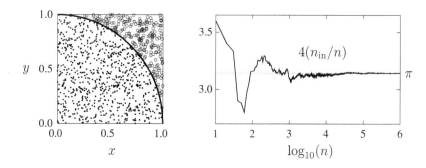

Fig. 11.2   Area of a circular quadrant and evaluation of π with pseudo-random numbers. Points inside the quadrants are shown as dots and points outside the quadrant are shown as open circles.

of the constant π. As depicted in Figure 11.2, a simple strategy is to estimate the fraction of the area that falls within the quadrant of the circle by randomly throwing points in the two-dimensional square (x, y). The probability of the random points to fall within the quadrant of the circle, n_{in}/n, should be equal to $\pi/4$. A simple extension of the method illustrated in Figure 11.2 could be the estimation of the area under an arbitrary curve generating a random set of points located inside a rectangle sufficiently large to contain the curve of interest, and counting the number of points that fell under the curve.

11.2   Simulating simple probability distributions

Equation (11.1) only generates R uniformly distributed in the interval $[0, 1]$. Straightforward extensions are possible. For example, a scaling procedure can be used, $x = LR$, to generate x uniformly distributed in the interval $[0, L]$. Similarly, a shifting procedure, $x = (R + d)$ can be used to generate x uniformly distributed in the interval $[d, 1 + d]$. Ultimately, having an algorithm to generate random numbers uniformly distributed in the interval $[0, 1]$ is nice, but only of limited use because we often need random numbers that follow other probability distributions. Therefore it is important to design ways to manipulate R for this purpose.

As an example, imagine that one is interested to simulate two states corresponding to probability $1/4$ and $3/4$. One could generate R uniformly distributed in the interval $[0, 1]$ and based on this information declare that if $0 < R < 0.25$, then the state if the system is set to 1, and if $0.25 < R < 1.0$, then the state if the system is set to 2. This procedure will automatically yield a state 1 with probability equal to $1/4$, and a state 2 with probability equal to $3/4$.

More generally, one may combine various subintervals $[0, 1]$ to ascribe different probabilities to any number of states. For example, to simulate four states with probability $p(i)$, with,

$$p(1) = 0.50$$

$$p(2) = 0.25$$

$$p(3) = 0.15$$

$$p(4) = 0.10$$

from the number R uniformly distributed with $[0, 1]$, one could use the following rule:

if $0.00 < R < 0.50$, then set the state i to 1

if $0.50 < R < 0.75$, then set the state i to 2

if $0.75 < R < 0.90$, then set the state i to 3

if $0.90 < R < 1.00$, then set the state i to 4

Intuitively, it is expected that the states 1 to 4 will have the correct probabilities because the random number R is uniformly distributed and, therefore, we can ascribe a subinterval in $[0, 1]$ that is proportional to the probability of each of the states i. In practice, what we did here is to construct the cumulative probability function $P(i)$, defined as,

$$P(1) = p(1)$$

$$P(2) = p(1) + p(2)$$

$$P(3) = p(1) + p(2) + p(3)$$

$$P(4) = p(1) + p(2) + p(3) + p(4)$$

or

$$P(i) = \sum_{j=1}^{i} p(j) \tag{11.3}$$

for i going from 1 to 4. The values of the cumulative probability function $P(i)$ are,

$$P(1) = 0.50$$
$$P(2) = 0.75$$
$$P(3) = 0.90$$
$$P(4) = 1.00$$

To pick a state i with the proper probability, one generates a random R distributed in the interval $[0, 1]$, and then matches this value with the constructed cumulative probability function $P(i)$. The operation to go from R to the state i, according to the rules of Eq. (11.3), is depicted graphically in Figure 11.3. This operation goes through the inverse of the cumulative probability function $i = P^{-1}(R)$.

These ideas can easily be extended to continuous random variables by considering the limit where there is a very large number of discrete states. Let us assume that we want to generate the random variable x that is distributed according to $p(x)$. Mathematically, the operation consists of considering the following equality,

$$p(x)dx = p(R)dR \tag{11.4}$$

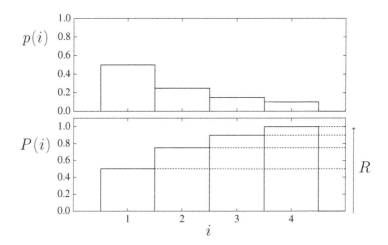

Fig. 11.3 Probability distribution $p(i)$ and cumulative probability function $P(i)$.

where $p(R)$ is uniformly distributed in the interval $[0, 1]$. By normalization, we have that $p(R) = 1$:

$$\int_{-\infty}^{x(R)} p(x') \, dx' = \int_0^{R(x)} dR$$

$$P(x(R)) = R \qquad (11.5)$$

$$x(R) = P^{-1}(R)$$

where the P^{-1} indicates the inverse function to the cumulative probability function P. It follows that the function $x(R)$ generates a random variable x such that it is distributed according to $p(x)$. The simple recipe is to take a uniformly distributed random R and insert it in the inverse function $P^{-1}(R)$ to generate the desired random x. This operation is depicted graphically in Figure 11.4.

One important case is a random variable x that is distributed exponentially in the interval $[0, \infty]$:

$$\int_x^{\infty} p(x) \, dx = a \int_x^{\infty} e^{-ax} \, dx$$

$$P(x) = e^{-ax} \Big|_{\infty}^{x}$$

$$= e^{-ax} \qquad (11.6)$$

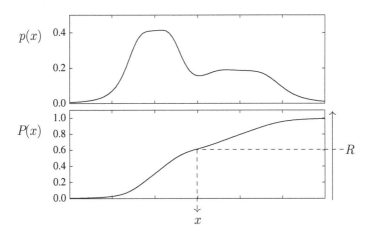

Fig. 11.4 Illustrative example depicting the reverse formula $x = P^{-1}(R)$ for generating random x distributed according to the probability $p(x)$.

Hence, $x = (-1/a) \ln(R)$, where R is a random number uniformly distributed within the interval $[0, 1]$. Exponentially distributed random variables are needed to simulate Markov processes. For example, if the mean survival time of a state is τ, the probability to survive in this state for a time t is $P(t) = e^{-t/\tau}$, which can be generated with $t = (-\tau) \ln(R)$.

Another very important example is the case of a Gaussian distributed random variable, $p(x) = e^{-x^2/2\sigma^2}/\sqrt{2\pi\sigma^2}$. This requires some special trickery because the integral of the Gaussian does not have a closed analytical form and the inverse function P^{-1} is not available. For the sake of simplicity, let us assume that the mean is zero. The problem is solved by considering the problem in two dimensions,

$$
\begin{aligned}
p(x)\,p(y)\,dx\,dy &= \frac{e^{-x^2/2\sigma^2}}{\sqrt{2\pi\sigma^2}}\,\frac{e^{-y^2/2\sigma^2}}{\sqrt{2\pi\sigma^2}}\,dx\,dy \\
&= \frac{e^{-r^2/2\sigma^2}}{\sigma^2}\,r\,dr\,\frac{d\theta}{2\pi} \\
&= p(r)r\,dr\,p(\theta)\,d\theta
\end{aligned}
\tag{11.7}
$$

where we introduced the polar coordinates,

$$
x = r\,\cos\theta \tag{11.8}
$$

$$
y = r\,\sin\theta \tag{11.9}
$$

To generate the Gaussian distributed random numbers x (or y), we need to generate a random radial distance r distributed according to $p(r)$ and a random angle θ distributed according to $p(\theta)$. Thus, two uniformly distributed random numbers will be required to generate x: one for r and one for θ. The normalized angular probability distribution $p(\theta)$ is uniform for $\theta \in [0, 2\pi]$,

$$
p(\theta) = \frac{1}{2\pi} \tag{11.10}
$$

and random angles θ obeying this distribution can easily be generated via a simple dilation, $\theta = 2\pi R$. The normalized radial probability distribution is

$$
p(r) = \frac{e^{-r^2/2\sigma^2}}{\sigma^2} \tag{11.11}
$$

which can be integrated from 0 to r to obtain the cumulative probability distribution,

$$P(r) = \int_0^{2\pi} \frac{d\theta}{2\pi} \int dr \, r \frac{e^{-r^2/2\sigma^2}}{\sigma^2}$$

$$= -\int_r^\infty d\left(e^{-r^2/2\sigma^2}\right)$$

$$= -\left.\left(e^{-r^2/2\sigma^2}\right)\right|_r^\infty$$

$$= e^{-r^2/2\sigma^2} \tag{11.12}$$

It follows that the random radial variable r can be generated with $r = P^{-1}(R) = \sigma\sqrt{-2\ln(R)}$. Accordingly, the Gaussian-distributed variable x is generated as,

$$x = \sigma\sqrt{-2\ln(R_1)} \, \cos(2\pi R_2) \tag{11.13}$$

where R_1 and R_2 are two independent random numbers uniformly distributed within the interval $[0, 1]$. Equivalently, it is also possible to use the same algorithm to generate a Gaussian-distributed random variable y,

$$y = \sigma\sqrt{-2\ln(R_2)} \, \sin(2\pi R_1) \tag{11.14}$$

This method to generate Gaussian-distributed variables is called the Box–Muller algorithm.

11.3 Activated dynamics

In the reactive flux formalism (see Section 9.2 in Chapter 9), the initial velocity of the ion along the reaction coordinate must be sampled from the non-Maxwellian velocity distribution:

$$v \, \theta(v) \, e^{-mv^2/2k_B T} \tag{11.15}$$

This is the distribution that is needed to generate the so-called "activated" trajectories with initial conditions based on Eq. (9.13). Such a distribution may be generated from normal random numbers R distributed between 0 and 1 using:

$$v = \left[\frac{-2k_B T}{m} \ln(R)\right]^{1/2} \tag{11.16}$$

while all other initial velocities are sampled from a Maxwell distribution at temperature T.

11.4 Metropolis Monte Carlo

A critical task of molecular simulations is to sample configurations according to the equilibrium Boltzmann distribution:

$$P_{\text{eq}}(x) \propto e^{-U(x)/k_{\text{B}}T} \tag{11.17}$$

If the distribution $P_{\text{eq}}(x)$ was available, then we could, in principle, compute any average we are interested in. But this distribution is not available explicitly. Generating random values of x followed by an estimation of the Boltzmann factor, $e^{-U(x)/k_{\text{B}}T}$, is completely impractical because of the wide variations in the value of the exponential function. Clearly, many values of x correspond to high energy configurations with very low probability.

To solve the problem, the Metropolis Monte Carlo method constructs a random walk in configuration space, $x \to x' \to x'' \to \cdots$, such that it converges toward the proper equilibrium distribution [Metropolis *et al.* (1953)]. To guarantee that the random walk will converge toward the proper distribution, we impose the condition of microscopic detailed balance on the transition probability $T_{x \to x'}$,

$$P_{\text{eq}}(x)T_{x \to x'} = P_{\text{eq}}(x')T_{x' \to x} \tag{11.18}$$

yielding the condition,

$$\frac{T_{x \to x'}}{T_{x' \to x}} = \frac{P_{\text{eq}}(x')}{P_{\text{eq}}(x)}$$
$$= e^{-[U(x')-U(x)]/k_{\text{B}}T} \tag{11.19}$$

It is helpful to separate the transition probability $T_{x \to x'}$ into two distinct steps. First, we consider the probability of an attempted or proposed "candidate" move, then we consider the probability of accepting or rejecting this candidate:

$$T_{x \to x'} = T^{\text{p}}_{x \to x'} \, T^{\text{a/r}}_{x \to x'} \tag{11.20}$$

For example, one of the simplest forms for the proposed move $T^{\text{p}}_{x \to x'}$ is to introduce a small random shift Δx such that $x' = x + \Delta x$. This can be constructed, for example, by using a uniformly distributed random number $R \in [0, 1]$ as,

$$x' = x + L\,(R - 0.5) \tag{11.21}$$

with the scale L chosen for optimal efficiency. It is important to note that the condition $T^{\mathrm{P}}_{x \to x'} = T^{\mathrm{P}}_{x' \to x}$ is satisfied because x' is symmetrically distributed around x. Alternatively, one could generate random Gaussian shifts Δx from a Box–Muller algorithm. The advantage of using the proposed symmetrically distributed transition probability is that it cancels out in the microscopic detailed balance condition Eq. (11.19),

$$\frac{T^{\mathrm{a/r}}_{x \to x'}}{T^{\mathrm{a/r}}_{x' \to x}} = e^{-[U(x')-U(x)]/k_{\mathrm{B}}T} \tag{11.22}$$

This implies that the probability to accept or reject the proposed move is quite simply related to the Boltzmann factor of the difference in energy $U(x') - U(x)$ associated with the proposed move. One possible way to satisfy Eq. (11.19) is the Metropolis method:

$$T^{\mathrm{a/r}}_{x \to x'} = \begin{cases} 1 & \text{if } U(x') < U(x) \\ e^{-[U(x')-U(x)]/k_{\mathrm{B}}T} & \text{if } U(x') > U(x) \end{cases} \tag{11.23}$$

The Metropolis Monte Carlo simulation consists in a large number of small steps in which one attempts to move a particle by a small shift via Eq. (11.21), then compare the energy $U(x')$ after this shift with the previous energy $U(x)$, and then use the probability Eq. (11.23) to accept or reject the proposed move. Practically, if the energy decreased, $U(x') < U(x)$, then the move is accepted. If the energy increased, $U(x') > U(x)$, then the move is accepted if $R < e^{-[U(x')-U(x)]/k_{\mathrm{B}}T}$, where R is a uniformly distributed random number $\in [0, 1]$. The move is rejected if $R > e^{-[U(x')-U(x)]/k_{\mathrm{B}}T}$. If the move is rejected, then the system is restored with the previous coordinate x. If the move is accepted, then the next steps proceed from the new coordinate x'.

11.5 Langevin dynamics

Langevin dynamics obeys the classical equation of motion,

$$m \frac{dv}{dt} = F - \gamma v + f(t) \tag{11.24}$$

where the force $f(t)$ is a Gaussian random variable with $\langle f(t) \rangle = 0$ and $\langle f(0) f(t) \rangle = 2k_{\mathrm{B}}T\gamma\delta(t)$. The systematic force $F = -\partial W/\partial x$ is the derivative of the potential $W(x)$ evaluated at $x(t)$. Integrating the equation of motion over a short time Δt yields,

$$\int_t^{t+\Delta t} \left(\frac{dv}{dt}\right) dt = \int_t^{t+\Delta t} \frac{F(x(t))}{m} dt - \int_t^{t+\Delta t} \frac{\gamma}{m} v dt + \frac{1}{m} \int_t^{t+\Delta t} f(t') dt'$$

$$v(t + \Delta t) - v(t) = \frac{F(x(t))}{m} \Delta t - \frac{\gamma}{m} v(t) \Delta t + g \qquad (11.25)$$

$$v(t + \Delta t) = v(t) + \frac{F(x(t))}{m} \Delta t - \frac{\gamma}{m} v(t) \Delta t + g$$

where g is

$$g = \frac{1}{m} \int_t^{t+\Delta t} f(t') dt' \qquad (11.26)$$

From the properties of the random force $f(t)$, we know that g is also a Gaussian random variable with average,

$$\langle g \rangle = \frac{1}{m} \int_t^{t+\Delta t} \langle f(t') \rangle dt'$$

$$= 0 \qquad (11.27)$$

and variance,

$$\langle g^2 \rangle = \frac{1}{m^2} \int_t^{t+\Delta t} \int_{-\infty}^{\infty} dt' dt'' \langle f(t') f(t'') \rangle$$

$$= \frac{1}{m^2} \int_t^{t+\Delta t} \int_{-\infty}^{\infty} dt' dt'' \, 2 k_{\mathrm{B}} T \gamma \delta(t' - t'')$$

$$= \frac{1}{m^2} 2 k_{\mathrm{B}} T \gamma \Delta t \qquad (11.28)$$

At each time-step, a random g of the appropriate magnitude can be generated from the Box–Muller algorithm,

$$g = \sqrt{\frac{2 k_{\mathrm{B}} T \gamma \Delta t}{m^2}} \sqrt{-2 \ln(R_1)} \cos(2\pi R_2) \qquad (11.29)$$

where R_1 and R_2 are two random numbers uniformly distributed within the interval $[0, 1]$. The new position $x(t + \Delta t)$ is obtained by integrating the velocity,

$$\int_t^{t+\Delta t} dx = \int_t^{t+\Delta t} dt v(t)$$

$$x(t + \Delta t) - x(t) = v(t)\Delta t \tag{11.30}$$

$$x(t + \Delta t) = x(t) + v(t)\Delta t$$

A more accurate Langevin dynamics algorithm combines the stochastic propagation from the random noise with the Verlet algorithm for the systematic forces [Brunger *et al.* (1984)].

11.6 Brownian dynamics

The simplest route to derive the equation for Brownian dynamics starts from the Langevin Eq. (11.24) and assumes that the inertial factor mdv/dt is negligible,

$$0 = F - \gamma v + f(t)$$

$$\gamma v(t) = F + f(t)$$

$$\frac{dx}{dt} = \frac{1}{\gamma} F + \frac{1}{\gamma} f(t) \tag{11.31}$$

$$\frac{dx}{dt} = \frac{D}{k_\mathrm{B} T} F + \xi(t)$$

where the Einstein relation, $\gamma = k_\mathrm{B} T / D$, has been used. The random noise $\xi(t)$ is defined as,

$$\xi(t) = \text{random noise} = \frac{1}{\gamma} f(t) \tag{11.32}$$

Because $f(t)$ is Gaussian, $\xi(t)$ is Gaussian too, with average $\langle \xi(t) \rangle = 0$, and

$$\langle \xi(t)\xi(0) \rangle = \frac{1}{\gamma^2} \langle f(t)f(0) \rangle$$

$$= \frac{1}{\gamma^2} 2 k_\mathrm{B} T \gamma \cdot \delta(t)$$

$$= 2 \left(\frac{k_\mathrm{B} T}{\gamma} \right) \delta(t)$$

$$= 2 D \delta(t) \tag{11.33}$$

It is possible to integrate Eq. (11.31),

$$\int_t^{t+\Delta t} \frac{dx}{dt} dt = \int_t^{t+\Delta t} \frac{D}{k_B T} F dt + \int_t^{t+\Delta t} \xi(t') dt'$$

$$x(t + \Delta t) - x(t) = \frac{DF}{k_B T} \Delta t + g$$

(11.34)

where g is a Gaussian-distributed random number with zero average and mean square deviation equal to $2D\Delta t$.

$$x(t + \Delta t) = x(t) + \left(\frac{DF(x(t))}{k_B T} \right) \Delta t + g$$

(11.35)

where g is a Gaussian-distributed random number given by:

$$g = (\sqrt{2D\Delta t}) \sqrt{-2\ln(R_1)} \cos(2\pi R_2)$$

(11.36)

If there were no external potential W, then the process would correspond to Gaussian-distributed random jumps of mean square deviation equal to $2D\Delta t$, which corresponds to a simple diffusion process. This derivation of the BD algorithm is only valid when the diffusion coefficient is independent of the position [Ermak (1975)]. As shown in Eq. (8.19), if the diffusion coefficient depends on position, then this algorithm needs to be modified to include the effect of a virtual "force-like" term,

$$x(t + \Delta t) = x(t) + \left(\frac{DF(x(t))}{k_B T} \right) \Delta t + \left(\frac{\partial D}{\partial x} \right) \Delta t + g$$

(11.37)

Otherwise there will a spurious drift of the particle affecting the dynamics.

11.7   Colored noise

So far, we have encountered only the simplest kind of time-dependent random signals. For example, the random forces entering the Langevin and Brownian dynamics algorithms (discussed in Sections 11.5 and 11.6) are essentially uncorrelated fluctuating random signals with no memory. This type of random signal is sometimes referred to as a "white noise" because it equally contains components at all possible frequencies. In contrast, the random force used in simulations based on the generalized Langevin equation is more complex. As shown in Section 7.7, this random force must satisfy the second fluctuation-dissipation theorem with respect to the memory function according to Eq. (7.56). This type of random signal is typically called "colored noise" because the contributions from various frequencies are different. It is important to have the ability to generate time-dependent random signals with prescribed statistical features. This is possible following a method proposed by Rice (1944, 1945).

Let us first consider the random signal $S(t)$ and its correlation function,

$$C(t) = \langle S(t' + t)S(t') \rangle \tag{11.38}$$

and its Fourier transform following Eq. (6.38),

$$\widetilde{C}(\omega) = 2 \int_0^\infty C(t) \cos(\omega t)\, dt \tag{11.39}$$

Following Eq. (6.39), the inverse transform is

$$C(t) = \frac{2}{2\pi} \int_0^\infty \widetilde{C}(\omega) \cos(\omega t)\, d\omega \tag{11.40}$$

To generate a random signal prescribed by a provided power spectrum, we start from a Fourier series representation of the signal $S(t)$ over a time interval $[0, \mathcal{T}]$,

$$S(t) = \sum_{n=1}^{N} a_n \cos(\omega_n t) + b_n \sin(\omega_n t) \tag{11.41}$$

where $t \in [0, \mathcal{T}]$ and $\omega_n = n\Delta\omega$, with $\Delta\omega = 2\pi/\mathcal{T}$. The Fourier coefficients a_n and b_n are assumed to be independent Gaussian variables with, $\langle a_n \rangle = \langle b_n \rangle = 0$, and $\langle a_n^2 \rangle = \langle b_n^2 \rangle = \sigma_n^2$ which can be generated from the Box–Muller algorithm. From the correlation function we know that

$$C(t) = \langle S(t' + t)S(t') \rangle$$

$$= \left\langle \left(\sum_{n=1}^{N} a_n \cos(\omega_n(t + t')) + b_n \sin(\omega_n(t + t')) \right)^2 \right\rangle$$

$$= \sum_{n=1}^{N} \langle a_n^2 \rangle \cos(\omega_n(t + t')) \cos(\omega_n t') + \langle b_n^2 \rangle \sin(\omega_n(t + t')) \sin(\omega_n t')$$

$$= \sum_{n=1}^{N} \sigma_n^2 \big(\cos(\omega_n(t + t')) \cos(\omega_n t') + \sin(\omega_n(t + t')) \sin(\omega_n t') \big)$$

$$= \sum_{n=1}^{N} \sigma_n^2 \cos(\omega_n t)$$

$$= \frac{2}{2\pi} \sum_{n=1}^{N} \widetilde{C}(\omega_n) \cos(\omega_n t)\, \Delta\omega \tag{11.42}$$

where $\cos(\alpha-\beta) = \cos(\alpha)\cos(\beta)+\sin(\alpha)\sin(\beta)$ was used. Equation (11.42) is the discrete form of the integral of Eq. (11.40). By identification, it follows that

$$\sigma_n^2 = \frac{2}{2\pi}\,\widetilde{C}(\omega_n)\Delta\omega \tag{11.43}$$

The colored noise can be constructed by first generating N Fourier coefficients from,

$$a_n = (\sigma_n)\sqrt{-2\ln(R_1)}\,\cos(2\pi R_2) \tag{11.44}$$

and

$$b_n = (\sigma_n)\sqrt{-2\ln(R_1)}\,\sin(2\pi R_2) \tag{11.45}$$

where σ_n is prescribed by the power spectrum through Eq. (11.43). From the set of coefficients a_n and b_n, the time-dependent random signal then can be reconstructed using Eq. (11.41) for a time t included in the interval $[0, \mathcal{T}]$. This can be accomplished via a direct sum, or using a fast Fourier transform algorithm.

11.8   Discrete-state continuous-time Markov chain

Let us first consider a simple two-state continuous-time Markov process,

$$A \underset{k_{B\to A}}{\overset{k_{A\to B}}{\rightleftharpoons}} B$$

As illustrated in Figure 11.5, the dynamical trajectory of this process consists in a sequence of temporary stays (sojourns) in the two states: ..., $A(t_1)$, $B(t_2)$, $A(t_3)$, $B(t_4)$, $A(t_5)$, $B(t_6)$, $A(t_7)$, $B(t_8)$, ... The stays correspond to a survival process and their distribution may be determined by the kinetic equations:

$$\frac{dP^A}{dt} = -k_{A\to B}P^A + k_{B\to A}P^B \tag{11.46}$$

$$\frac{dP^B}{dt} = k_{A\to B}P^A - k_{B\to A}P^B \tag{11.47}$$

For example, if we assume that we start in state A, the probability to have remained in this state without any transition for a time t is obtained by

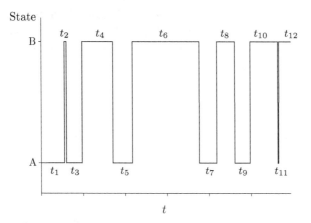

Fig. 11.5 Trajectory of a two-state Markov model. The rate from A to B is 3 per unit of time, and the rate from B to A is 2 per unit of time.

setting $k_{B \to A}$ to zero in Eq. (11.46), yielding,

$$\frac{dP^A}{dt} = -k_{A \to B}P^A \tag{11.48}$$

the solution is $P^A(t) = e^{-k_{A \to B}t}$. Thus, the survival time in state A is exponentially distributed, and a random stay can be generated as

$$t = -\left(\frac{1}{k_{A \to B}}\right)\ln(R) \tag{11.49}$$

Similarly, a random stay in state B can be generated as

$$t = -\left(\frac{1}{k_{B \to A}}\right)\ln(R) \tag{11.50}$$

Generating a random trajectory of the process with the sequence $\{A(t_1), B(t_2), A(t_3), B(t_4), A(t_5), B(t_6), \dots\}$; thus, requires the exponentially distributed random times in state A $(t_1, t_3, t_5, t_7, \dots)$, and in state B $(t_2, t_4, t_6, t_8, \dots)$. This method is often called kinetic Monte Carlo or Gillespie algorithm [Gillespie (1976)]. A critical aspect of this algorithm is that it does not require a time-step to simulate a trajectory of the system.

The simulation of a Markov model with multiple states defined by the transition matrix $\mathbf{Q}$ can be treated according to the same general rules, with additional features to handle the state-to-state branching. The random survival time t in the state i is generated by,

$$t = \frac{1}{Q(i,i)} \ln(R) \qquad (11.51)$$

where the matrix Q_{ii} element defined by Eq. (10.18):

$$Q_{ii} = -\sum_{s \neq i}^{j} Q_{is} \qquad (11.52)$$

corresponds to the negative sum of all the outgoing transition rates from the state i. After a random stay of length τ in the state i, the branching probability to make a transition to state j is generated by:

$$\text{Loop over } j = 1, N$$

$$\text{if } \{R \leq P_{\mathrm{t}}(j)\} \text{ then transit to state } j \qquad (11.53)$$

where

$$P_{\mathrm{t}}(j) = \sum_{k \neq i}^{j} \frac{Q_{ik}}{-Q_{ii}} \qquad (11.54)$$

is the cumulative probability for the branching process. As demonstrated in Section 10.3, this algorithm generates random trajectories that are consistent with the time-dependent probability of the discrete-state continuous-time Markov chain. As an illustration, let us consider the dynamics of a three-state Markov process defined by,

$$A \underset{k_2}{\overset{k_1}{\rightleftharpoons}} B \underset{k_4}{\overset{k_3}{\rightleftharpoons}} C$$

where the rate constants are: $k_1 = 5\mathrm{s}^{-1}$, $k_2 = 1\mathrm{s}^{-1}$, $k_3 = 12\mathrm{s}^{-1}$, and $k_4 = 15\mathrm{s}^{-1}$. The time course of the process is shown in Figure 11.6. The rapid interconversion of the states B and C is interrupted by the slower transition from B to C.

11.9   Combined BD and Markov model

As the final illustration, it is of interest to show how different elements like BD and a discrete-state continuous-time Markov chain can be combined

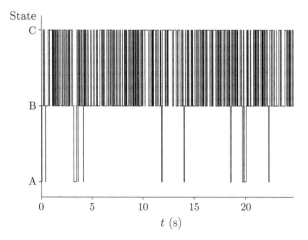

Fig. 11.6 Plot of the time course of the three-state Markov model A $\rightleftharpoons$ B $\rightleftharpoons$ C. The mean lifetimes are 0.2, 0.077, and 0.066 s for states A, B, and C, respectively. Averaging over the trajectory yields the equilibrium probability $P_A = 1/(1 + 5 + 40 = 0.1$, $P_B = 5/(1 + 5 + 4) = 0.5$, and $P_C = 4/(1 + 5 + 4) = 0.4$.

to construct models of increasing sophistication. For example, one could imagine a particle undergoing motions along the x-axis with random transitions between two potential surfaces, $W_1(x)$ and $W_2(x)$. This type of model may be useful to represent systems that display a combination of long-term memory effects that cannot be adequately approximated by simple BD. The algorithm comprises the standard time-step of BD:

$$x(t + \Delta t) = x(t) + \left(\frac{D_i}{k_B T} \right) F_i(x(t)) \Delta t + g_i \qquad (11.55)$$

where $F_i(x) = -W_i'(x)$, and g_i is a state-dependent Gaussian-distributed random number given by:

$$g_i = (\sqrt{2D_i \Delta t}) \sqrt{-2 \ln(R_1)} \cos(2\pi R_2) \qquad (11.56)$$

In addition, the system can hop from state i to state j according to the transition probability:

$$\text{if } \{R \leq k_{ij}(x) \Delta t\}, \text{ then transit to state } j \qquad (11.57)$$

Note that it is not possible to use Eqs. (11.49) and (11.50) to generate exponentially distributed times because the transition rates keep changing as the particle moves along the x-axis. A typical trajectory of a two-state

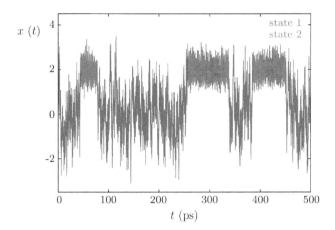

Fig. 11.7   Plot of the time course of the combined BD with the two-state Markov model. When the system is in state 1 (red), the PMF, $W_1(x) = \frac{1}{2} K_1 (x-2)^2$ and the force is $F_1(x) = -K_1(x-2)$. When the system is in state 2 (blue), the PMF, $W_2(x) = \frac{1}{2} K_2 x^2$, and the force is $F_2(x) = -K_2 x$. The position x is in Å. The force constants K_1 and K_2 are 10 and 1 $k_B T/\text{Å}^{-2}$, respectively. The diffusion constant D_1 and D_2 are both equal to 1 $\text{Å}^2 \text{ps}^{-1}$. Propagation was carried out from Eqs. (11.55) and (11.57). The transition rates were calculated from Eqs. (11.59) and (11.60) with $k_0 = 0.03\,\text{ps}^{-1}$.

system is shown in Figure 11.7. It is important to note that the transition rates between the two states of the system must satisfy the microscopic detailed balance for all values of x,

$$p_1(x)k_{12}(x) = p_2(x)k_{21}(x) \tag{11.58}$$

There are multiple ways to satisfy this condition. For the sake of simplicity, one could assume that the transition rates take the form,

$$k_{12}(x) = k_0\, e^{-[W_2(x)-W_1(x)]/2k_B T} \tag{11.59}$$

and

$$k_{21}(x) = k_0\, e^{-[W_1(x)-W_2(x)]/2k_B T} \tag{11.60}$$

But other valid recipes are possible. In general, the physical situation of interest should further constrain the modeling of the transition rates.

Chapter 12

Molecular machines

The previous chapters provided a broad overview of the theoretical foundations that underlie many important concepts such as marginal distribution, potential of mean force, free energy, continuum electrostatics, Poisson–Boltzmann theory, ionic screening, binding constants, effective dynamics of reduced models, diffusion processes, transition rates, and Markov chains. These various conceptual elements, can be creatively combined together as "building blocks" to construct models representative of complex macromolecular "machines." Calling them in this manner is not merely a metaphor: they are very much like real machines, using energy to change their shape, drive motion, and do useful work.

Molecular machines are complex biomolecules, proteins, nucleic acids, and carbohydrates that consume energy in order to perform specific and critical biological functions. The concerted action of all those machines underlies the activities of a living cell. Prominent examples are ribosomes, chromatophores, ion channels, pumps, polymerases, chaperones, kinases, actins and myosins, membrane transporters, ATP synthetases, and many more. Molecular machines typically need to change their shape and go through different conformational states to perform their function, mostly through complex allosteric mechanisms. To understand how they are able to perform their function, it is necessary to identify the different moving parts and understand how they act together. This requires detailed knowledge about those conformational states as well as of the pathways connecting them.

Ultimately, the purpose of a model should not only be viewed as a tool to predict and interpret functional outcomes, but also as a conceptual framework presenting an integrated picture of the system of interest to further guide our perception and articulate the key factors that are at play.

In that sense, good models have tremendous pedagogical value and importance. Breaking new ground with these difficult problems will require novel paradigms permitting seamless integration of structural, dynamical and functional data from experiments and theory. The field is obviously much too vast to cover all that is possible. We must, therefore, limit ourselves to a few illustrative systems. Using membrane transport as a paradigm, we will first review the main ingredients involved in the construction of multistate models. We will then briefly discuss the conceptual structure of models representing key biological systems.

12.1 Uniporter

Many of the basic ingredients needed to build a model of a molecular machine can be illustrated by considering a simple membrane transporter (sometimes called a facilitator). A uniporter is a transport protein that helps facilitate the movement of a substrate molecule across the cell membrane in response to a chemical gradient. For example, the glucose transporter 1 (or GLUT1) is a uniporter protein that facilitates the transport of glucose across the plasma membranes of mammalian cells [Galochkina *et al.* (2019)]. Many of those membrane transport proteins function according to an alternating access model of transport [Jardetzky (1966)], in which the protein switches conformations to present the substrate-binding site to alternate sides of the membrane without ever fully opening a direct pathway from one side to the other (to prevent undesirable leaks).

The simplest possible model with alternating access is depicted in Figure 12.1. The model comprises three states. One state corresponds to the protein without substrate, while the two other states correspond to the protein with a bound substrate on each side of the membrane. The dynamics of the system and the conformational change are incorporated into three reversible transitions, yielding a total of six transition rate constants. For the sake of the discussion, let us consider, as a first step, the transition from state 1 to state 2, with the rate k_{12}, which represents the association of the substrate on the extracellular side of the membrane. The reverse transition from state 2 to state 1, with the rate k_{21}, represents the dissociation of the substrate from the protein on the extracellular side of the membrane (out). The second step is the transition from state 2 to state 3, with the rate k_{23}, which corresponds to the conformational change of the protein associated with the internal translocation of the substrate from the extracellular to the intracellular side of the membrane. The reverse process is the transition from state 3 to state 2 with a rate of k_{32}. Finally, the last and

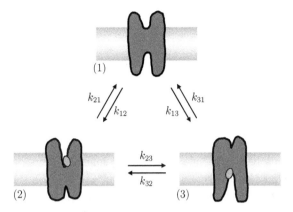

Fig. 12.1 Simple three-state model of an alternating access uniporter facilitating the permeation of a substrate from the extracellular side (labeled "out") to the intracellular side ("in"). The extracellular side is above the membrane and the intracellular side is below the membrane. The substrate concentration on the extracellular side is C^{out} and the substrate concentration on the intracellular side is C^{in}. Very similar models have been constructed to describe the ionic current through membrane channels [Läuger (1973)].

third step is the transition from state 3 to state 1 with the rate k_{32}, which corresponds to the release and dissociation of the substrate on the intracellular side (in) and the return of the protein back to its initial state. Again, the reverse transition from state 1 to state 2, with the rate k_{13}, represents the association of the substrate to the protein on the intracellular side of the membrane. The kinetic equations for the model are

$$\dot{P}_1 = -(k_{12} + k_{13})P_1 + k_{21}P_2 + k_{31}P_3$$
$$\dot{P}_2 = k_{12}P_1 - (k_{21} + k_{23})P_2 + k_{32}P_3 \qquad (12.1)$$
$$\dot{P}_3 = k_{13}P_1 + k_{23}P_2 - (k_{32} + k_{31})P_3$$

The requirement set by the model is the conservation of probability, $P_1 + P_2 + P_3 = 1$. For this reason, $\dot{P}_1 + \dot{P}_2 + \dot{P}_3 = 0$. This condition is clearly satisfied because the sum of the three lines Eq. (12.1) is equal to 0. This is a special case of the general condition previously encountered with Eq. (10.20).

Physically, the rates k_{12} and k_{13} correspond to a bimolecular association process. We saw in Section 9.6 how to formulate the problem of a bimolecular rate of encounter of two molecules in solution. While the present situation of a membrane protein is considerably more complicated than the simple generic spherical target immersed in an isotropic solution that led to Eq. (9.43), it is reasonable to assume that the rates k_{12} and k_{13} will have the overall form,

$$k_{12} = k_{\text{ass}}^{\text{out}} \, C^{\text{out}} \tag{12.2}$$

and

$$k_{13} = k_{\text{ass}}^{\text{in}} \, C^{\text{in}} \tag{12.3}$$

The constants $k_{\text{ass}}^{\text{out}}$ and $k_{\text{ass}}^{\text{in}}$ depend on the molecular detail of access to the two different binding pockets exposed to the extracellular and intracellular solutions. If the protein is not structurally symmetric then $k_{\text{ass}}^{\text{out}}$ and $k_{\text{ass}}^{\text{in}}$ are not necessarily identical. The dissociation rate of the substrate from the binding pocket on the extracellular side is k_{21}. As we have seen previously with Eq. (9.49), if the association and dissociation process are in equilibrium (ignoring the remaining states for now), this leads to an equilibrium binding constant for the extracellular side:

$$K_{\text{b}}^{\text{out}} = \frac{k_{\text{ass}}^{\text{out}}}{k_{21}} \tag{12.4}$$

There is a similar expression for the equilibrium binding constant on the intracellular side:

$$K_{\text{b}}^{\text{in}} = \frac{k_{\text{ass}}^{\text{in}}}{k_{21}} \tag{12.5}$$

Again, if the protein is not structurally symmetric then the two binding constants are not necessarily identical.

Let us now return to the kinetic equations Eq. (12.1). Under equilibrium conditions, all the time-derivatives $\dot{P}_i$ are set to 0. If we impose microscopic detailed balance under equilibrium conditions:

$$
\begin{aligned}
k_{12} P_1^{\text{eq}} &= k_{21} P_2^{\text{eq}} \\
k_{23} P_2^{\text{eq}} &= k_{32} P_3^{\text{eq}} \\
k_{31} P_3^{\text{eq}} &= k_{13} P_1^{\text{eq}}
\end{aligned}
\tag{12.6}
$$

it follows that

$$k_{12} \, k_{23} \, k_{31} \; \cancel{P_1^{\text{eq}} P_2^{\text{eq}} P_3^{\text{eq}}} = k_{21} \, k_{32} \, k_{13} \; \cancel{P_2^{\text{eq}} P_3^{\text{eq}} P_1^{\text{eq}}} \tag{12.7}$$

One may note that the product of the transition rates in the clockwise direction ($k_{21} k_{32} k_{13}$) is equal to the product of the transition rates in the anticlockwise direction ($k_{12}k_{23}k_{31}$). What this means is that the total free energy accumulated from the state-to-state increment of each transition must be zero, irrespective of whether one is going around the cycle in the clockwise or anticlockwise direction.

For a neutral substrate, equilibrium can be established with symmetric concentration, $C_{\text{out}} = C_{\text{in}} = C$. Specifically, this means that

$$\left(\frac{k_{\text{ass}}^{\text{out}} C}{k_{21}}\right)\left(\frac{k_{23}}{k_{32}}\right)\left(\frac{k_{31}}{k_{\text{ass}}^{\text{in}} C}\right) = 1$$

$$K_{\text{eq}}^{\text{out}}\left(\frac{k_{23}}{k_{32}}\right) = K_{\text{b}}^{\text{in}}$$

(12.8)

This analysis of the equilibrium situation shows that there is an underlying relation between the equilibrium binding constants on the intracellular and extracellular sides. The total equilibrium binding constant of the substrate to the receptor is $K_{\text{eq}}^{\text{out}} + K_{\text{eq}}^{\text{in}}$. As shown in Section 5.2, it is convenient to express the equilibrium probabilities as a Boltzmann-weighted sum over states. Let the free energy of state 1 be G_1, the free energy of state 2 be $G_2 = G_1 - k_{\text{B}}T\ln(K_{\text{b}}^{\text{out}} C)$, and the free energy of state 3 be $G_3 = G_1 - k_{\text{B}}T\ln(K_{\text{b}}^{\text{in}} C)$. Thus, the equilibrium probability of the states is

$$P_1^{\text{eq}} = \frac{1}{1 + (K_{\text{eq}}^{\text{out}} + K_{\text{eq}}^{\text{in}}) C}$$

$$P_2^{\text{eq}} = \frac{K_{\text{eq}}^{\text{out}} C}{1 + (K_{\text{eq}}^{\text{out}} + K_{\text{eq}}^{\text{in}}) C}$$

$$P_3^{\text{eq}} = \frac{K_{\text{eq}}^{\text{out}} C}{1 + (K_{\text{eq}}^{\text{out}} + K_{\text{eq}}^{\text{in}}) C}$$

(12.9)

These expressions may be further simplified using Eq. (12.8).

Now, let us examine the features of the model under nonequilibrium steady-state conditions, with $\dot{P}_i = 0$. The net flux ϕ_i for each step i is the forward flux of probability minus the backward flux of probability,

$$\Phi_{12} = P_1 k_{12} - P_2 k_{21}$$

$$\Phi_{31} = P_3 k_{31} - P_1 k_{13}$$

$$\Phi_{23} = P_2 k_{23} - P_3 k_{32}$$

(12.10)

Again, all the time derivatives $\dot{P}_i$ are again set to 0, but now there can be a net steady-state flux. The probability fluxes may be put in relation with the kinetic equations Eq. (12.1),

$$\dot{P}_1 = 0 = -\Phi_{12} + \Phi_{31}$$

$$\dot{P}_2 = 0 = \Phi_{12} - \Phi_{23} \tag{12.11}$$

$$\dot{P}_3 = 0 = -\Phi_{31} + \Phi_{13}$$

showing that all the fluxes cancel out, which is necessary under steady-state conditions. Under state-state conditions, all those fluxes must be the same. In the following, we will omit the subscript on Φ for the sake of simplicity.

Analysis of the steady-state solution would show that the rate of substrate transport depends on C^{in} and C^{out}. Obviously, $\phi = 0$ if the concentrations are the same. At low concentration, the system obeys linear response:

$$\Phi = \mathcal{P}\left(C^{\text{out}} - C^{\text{in}}\right) \tag{12.12}$$

where $\mathcal{P}$ is the permeability coefficient

$$\frac{1}{\mathcal{P}} = \frac{1}{k_{\text{ass}}^{\text{out}}} + \frac{1}{K_{\text{b}}^{\text{out}} k_{23}} + \frac{1}{k_{\text{ass}}^{\text{in}}} \tag{12.13}$$

(note that the central term could also be expressed as $1/K_{\text{b}}^{\text{in}} k_{32}$). As the sum in Eq. (12.13) is dominated by the smallest rates, the expression is somewhat reminiscent of adding resistances in series. The maximum throughput is obtained by setting $C^{\text{in}} = 0$ and increasing C^{out} to saturation. This yields:

$$\Phi_{\max} = \left(\frac{1}{k_{23}} + \frac{k_{32}}{k_{23}k_{31}} + \frac{1}{k_{31}}\right)^{-1} \tag{12.14}$$

independently of concentration. If the dissociation rate is rapid then the rate of transport is primarily controlled by the translocation step k_{23}. If the association/dissociation steps on the extracellular side are fast compared to the internal translocation step and the dissociation step on the intracellular side, then a local binding equilibrium is established and the net flux becomes,

$$\Phi = \frac{K_{\text{b}}^{\text{out}} C^{\text{out}}}{1 + K_{\text{b}}^{\text{out}} C^{\text{out}}} k_{23} \tag{12.15}$$

Determining the steady-state solution of arbitrary models can become tedious. A useful numerical strategy is to express the problem,

$$
\begin{aligned}
0 &= -(k_{13} + k_{12})\, P_1^{ss} + & k_{21}\ & P_2^{ss} + & k_{31}\ & P_3^{ss} \\
0 &= \quad k_{12}\ & P_1^{ss} - (k_{21} + k_{23})\, P_2^{ss} + & k_{32}\ & P_3^{ss} \\
0 &= \quad k_{13}\ & P_1^{ss} + & k_{23}\ & P_2^{ss} - (k_{32} + k_{31})\, P_3^{ss}
\end{aligned} \tag{12.16}
$$

in matrix form

$$
\begin{pmatrix} 0 \\ 0 \\ 0 \end{pmatrix} = \mathbf{Q}\,\mathbf{P}^{ss} \tag{12.17}
$$

where the matrix elements, Q_{ij}, are the transition rates from i to j. We also have a normalization condition, $P_1^{ss} + P_2^{ss} + P_3^{ss} = 1$. The determinant of $\mathbf{Q}$ is zero because the sum over all the lines cancels out (due to microscopic detailed balance). To solve the problem, we substitute one line in $\mathbf{Q}$ by the normalization condition, $\mathbf{Q} \rightarrow \mathbf{Q}'$, yielding:

$$
\mathbf{Q}'\mathbf{P}^{ss} = \begin{pmatrix} 1 \\ 0 \\ 0 \end{pmatrix}
$$

$$
\mathbf{P}^{ss} = [\mathbf{Q}']^{-1} \begin{pmatrix} 1 \\ 0 \\ 0 \end{pmatrix}
\tag{12.18}
$$

Once we have the steady-state solution $\mathbf{P}^{ss}$, it is easy to compute the net flux through one branch of the system,

$$
\Phi = P_2^{ss}\, k_{23} - P_3^{ss}\, k_{32} \tag{12.19}
$$

Additional microscopic features may be incorporated into such models. An important factor, for example, is how the various steps associated with movements of charged moieties either from the substrate or the protein itself, could be coupled to the transmembrane potential V_{mp}. In a fashion that has some similarities to the Brønsted Φ-value analysis discussed in Section 9.5, the perturbation from the transmembrane potential is often introduced as a linear perturbation on the potential mean force (PMF) along the reaction coordinate:

$$
W(x; V_{mp}) = W(x; 0) + Q(x)\, V_{mp} \tag{12.20}
$$

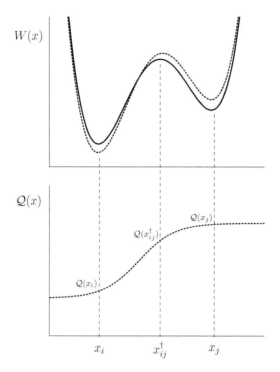

Fig. 12.2   Transition rates and coupling to a membrane potential. (Top) Schematic representation of the potential of mean force $W(x)$ governing the $i \to j$ and $j \to i$ transitions. The PMF in the absence (solid line) and in the presence (dashed line) of the membrane potential is shown. (Bottom) The quantity $\mathcal{Q}(x)$ is the effective charge, which provides the coupling of the system to the membrane potential V_{mp}.

where $\mathcal{Q}(x)$ is the fractional gating charge associated with the reaction coordinate x (although $\mathcal{Q}(x)$ does not have to be a linear function of x). The situation is illustrated in Figure 12.2. The effective charge $\mathcal{Q}$ was introduced in Eq. (4.29) in Chapter 4. It represents the coupling of the system to the transmembrane potential along the reaction coordinate x. The activation free energy for the $i \to j$ transition is,

$$\Delta W^{\dagger}_{i \to j} = W(x^{\dagger}_{ij}) - W(x_i)$$
$$= W(x^{\dagger}_{ij}; 0) - W(x_i; 0) + \left[\mathcal{Q}(x^{\dagger}_{ij}) - \mathcal{Q}(x_i) \right] V_{\mathrm{mp}} \qquad (12.21)$$

where $x_{ij}^\dagger$ represents the top of the energy barrier between the states i and j (by definition, $x_{ij}^\dagger = x_{ji}^\dagger$). The transition rate can be expressed as,

$$k_{ij} = k_{ij}^0 \, e^{-\Delta \mathcal{Q}_{ij}^\dagger V_{\mathrm{mp}}/k_{\mathrm{B}}T} \qquad (12.22)$$

where k_{ij}^0 is the transition rate in the absence of transmembrane potential, and

$$\Delta \mathcal{Q}_{ij}^\dagger = \mathcal{Q}(x_{ij}^\dagger) - \mathcal{Q}(x_i) \qquad (12.23)$$

is the effective charge movement associated with the transition. Importantly, the ratio of forward and backward transition rates obeys,

$$\frac{k_{ij}}{k_{ji}} = \frac{k_{ij}^0}{k_{ji}^0} \, e^{-[\Delta \mathcal{Q}_{ij}^\dagger - \Delta \mathcal{Q}_{ji}^\dagger] V_{\mathrm{mp}}/k_{\mathrm{B}}T}$$

$$= \frac{k_{ij}^0}{k_{ji}^0} \, e^{-[\mathcal{Q}(x_j) - \mathcal{Q}(x_i)] V_{\mathrm{mp}}/k_{\mathrm{B}}T} \qquad (12.24)$$

depends on the difference of the gating charge between the stable states i and j (the value of $\mathcal{Q}$ at the transition state $x_{ji}^\dagger$ drops out). While Eq. (12.24) imposes a sum-rule over the effective charge increments of forward and backward transitions, they may display very different dependence on the transmembrane potential. In that sense, $\Delta \mathcal{Q}_{ij}^\dagger$ and $\Delta \mathcal{Q}_{ji}^\dagger$ do not have to be necessarily equal. In fact, strong asymmetries are possible. For example, while the equilibrium binding constant may depend on the membrane potential:

$$K_{\mathrm{b}} = \frac{k_{\mathrm{ass}}^{\mathrm{out}}}{k_{\mathrm{diss}}}$$

$$= K_{\mathrm{b}}^0 \, e^{-[\mathcal{Q}_{\mathrm{b}} - \mathcal{Q}_{\mathrm{u}}] V_{\mathrm{mp}}/k_{\mathrm{B}}T} \qquad (12.25)$$

where $\mathcal{Q}_{\mathrm{b}} - \mathcal{Q}_{\mathrm{u}}$ is the effective charge gained between the bound and unbound states, the association rate k_{ass} and dissociation rate k_{diss} may display very different dependence on the membrane potential. As illustrated in Figure 12.3, if the bimolecular association rate is primarily controlled by random diffusion in solution (as in Eq. (9.43)), then k_{ass} may be fairly insensitive to V_{mp}. In this case, the unimolecular dissociation step corresponding to the substrate leaving its binding pocket, would incorporate the entire dependence on V_{mp}.

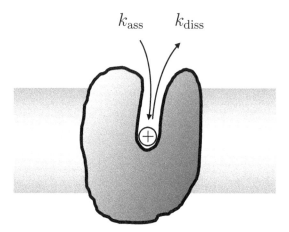

Fig. 12.3 Association and dissociation of a charged substrate to a site of a membrane protein located at the bottom of a deep crevice. While the equilibrium binding constant K_b may display a strong dependence on the membrane potential V_{mp}, the association rate k_{ass} will not depend on V_{mp} if the binding process is controlled by diffusion (no free energy barrier opposing binding). All the dependence in V_{mp} is then incorporated into the dissociation rate k_{diss}.

12.2   Coupled transport of multiple substrates

The model depicted in Figure 12.1 represents a simple passive transport system: the protein serves only as a catalyst by lowering the free energy barrier presented by the cell membrane to help the substrate move in the direction imposed by the difference between the extracellular and intracellular concentrations, C^{out} and C^{in}. There is a passive inward flux of substrate in the direction out→in only if $C^{out} > C^{out}$. By analogy to the analysis from Section 3.1 in Chapter 3, the passage of one molecule from the high concentration side to the low concentration side corresponds to a free energy difference of $-\Delta G$

$$\Delta G = k_B T \ln \left[\frac{C^{out}}{C^{in}} \right] \tag{12.26}$$

Thus, the substrate passively moves downhill in free energy, from the high to the low concentration region. For the charged substrate, the effect of the membrane potential also contributes to the change in free energy. Such passive membrane transport protein is sometimes called a facilitator, or uniporter.

    More complex systems aimed at transporting a substrate against its concentration gradient must couple their action to a free energy source.

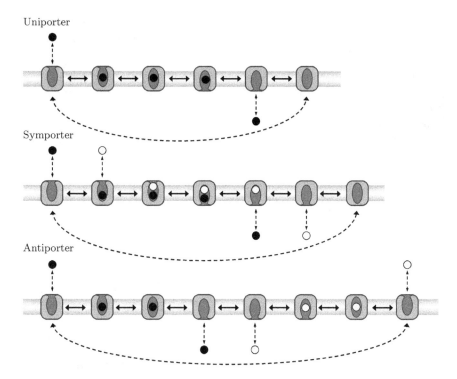

Fig. 12.4 Schematic multistate models of membrane transport systems based on the general alternating access mechanism in which the substrate-binding sites are exposed to either side of the membrane through a protein conformational change [Jardetzky (1966)]. All the transitions are represented by double arrows indicative of their reversibility. The alternating access mechanism provides a useful conceptual framework to explain the nonequilibrium transport of two or more substrates in the same direction (symporter) or in opposite directions (antiporter) [Forrest *et al.* (2011)]. An important example of symporters is the sodium symporter (NSS) family of membrane proteins, which are responsible for the reuptake of neurotransmitters from the synaptic cleft [Razavi *et al.* (2017)]. An example of an antiporter, displaying a H^+–Cl^{-1} exchange mechanism, is provided by the CLC protein [Feng *et al.* (2012)]. In contrast, a uniporter can only serve to facilitate the transport of a single substrate in an inward direction.

One possibility is to have a mechanism transporting two substrates simultaneously, one going uphill and the other one going downhill. For example, in a symporter, the two substrates are co-transported in the same direction, whereas they are co-transported in opposite directions in an antiporter. This is typically explained in terms of the alternating access mechanism illustrated in Figure 12.4. In many cases, the inward transport of amino acid or neurotransmitters will be powered by the downhill movement of one or a few Na^+ ions. This is an advantageous source of free energy, with a membrane potential of about -80 mV together with an extracellular concentration of about 150 mM compared to an intracellular concentration of about 2–3 mM.

It is possible to construct models of increasing levels of sophistication to represent the action of these transporter systems (Figure 12.4). While the details of such models may obscure the underlying fundamental principles, these systems ultimately exploit an interplay of the transport function equilibria. To clarify how this works, let us consider a transport system with a substrate A:

$$A_{\text{out}} \rightleftharpoons A_{\text{in}}$$

and a substrate B:

$$B_{\text{out}} \rightleftharpoons B_{\text{in}}$$

If they were independent from one another, the natural equilibrium of each substrate would obey,

$$\frac{[A_{\text{in}}]}{[A_{\text{out}}]} = K_{\text{eq}}^{A} \tag{12.27}$$

$$\frac{[B_{\text{in}}]}{[B_{\text{out}}]} = K_{\text{eq}}^{B} \tag{12.28}$$

The natural equilibrium constant across the cell membrane is 1 for a neutral substrate, but is $K_{\text{eq}} = e^{-qV_{\text{mp}}/k_{\text{B}}T}$ for a substrate carrying a charge q (the cellular membrane potential is typically on the order of -70 mV). This situation is depicted in Figure 12.5 (left). The joint equilibrium for the two uncoupled substrates may be expressed as,

$$A_{\text{out}} + B_{\text{out}} \rightleftharpoons A_{\text{in}} + B_{\text{in}}$$

In the absence of the transport protein, the overall equilibrium of the system would directly follow from Eqs. (12.27) and (12.28),

$$\frac{[A_{\text{in}}]}{[A_{\text{out}}]} \frac{[B_{\text{in}}]}{[B_{\text{out}}]} = K_{\text{eq}}^{A} K_{\text{eq}}^{B} \tag{12.29}$$

because each substrate follows its own natural equilibrium. Let us assume that the goal is to actively transport the substrate A from a low extracellular concentration to a higher intracellular concentration. The effective equilibrium that can be achieved is,

$$\frac{[A_{\text{in}}]}{[A_{\text{out}}]} = K_{\text{eq}}^{A} K_{\text{eq}}^{B} \frac{[B_{\text{out}}]}{[B_{\text{cell-in}}]} \tag{12.30}$$

In other words, the transport results from the law of mass action together with the cellular conditions. This situation is depicted in

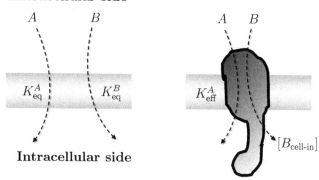

Extracellular side

Intracellular side

Fig. 12.5 Schematic illustration of the thermodynamic effect of coupling the transmembrane movement of two substrates A and B via a symporter transport protein. On the left, there is no protein and the equilibria of the two substrates are reached independently. On the right, the coupling drives the system to achieve an effective equilibrium constant K_{eff}^A for the substrate A.

Figure 12.5 (right). This analysis shows that the effective equilibrium constant of the substrate A will now be:

$$K_{\text{eff}}^A = K_{\text{eq}}^A \, K_{\text{eq}}^B \, \frac{[B_{\text{out}}]}{[B_{\text{cell-in}}]} \qquad (12.31)$$

which can be much larger than 1 depending on the situation. For example, if the primary substrate A is neutral and the secondary substrate is a positively charged Na^+ ion, the effective equilibrium constant will be

$$K_{\text{eff}}^A = e^{-qV_{\text{mp}}/k_B T} \, \frac{[Na]_{\text{out}}}{[Na]_{\text{cell-in}}}$$

$$= e^{(1.6 \, \text{kcal/mol})/k_B T} \, \frac{150 \, \text{mM}}{3 \, \text{mM}}$$

$$= 744 \qquad (12.32)$$

(assuming that $V_{\text{mp}} = -70 \, \text{mV}$). The implication is that the coupling could enable the system to actively transport the substrate A inside the cell up to 744 times the extracellular concentration. Remarkably, if n Na^+ ions are co-transported with the substrate A, its concentration inside the cell could increase by more than 744^n times the extracellular concentration. However, the system does not have the capacity to transport a substrate beyond this point — this is a fundamental thermodynamic constraint that must be inherently part of any model. While this discussion was carried out in the context of a symporter co-transporting two substrates in the same direction, the analysis also applies to antiporters co-transporting two substrates in opposite directions (Figure 12.5).

12.3 Coupling to a chemical reaction

Similar thermodynamic principles apply when the transport process is coupled to a chemical reaction occurring inside the cell,

$$M \rightleftharpoons M^*$$

with a natural equilibrium constant greatly favoring the production of M^* from M,

$$\frac{[M^*]}{[M]} = K_{eq}^M \gg 1 \qquad (12.33)$$

In the absence of the transport protein, the chemical production of M^* and the movement of A across the membrane each obey their own equilibrium independently. This situation is depicted in Figure 12.6 (left).

Extracellular side

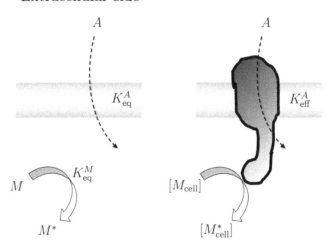

Intracellular side

Fig. 12.6 Schematic illustration of the thermodynamic effect of coupling the transmembrane movement of a substrate A and a chemical reaction of a molecule M via the transport protein. On the left, there is no protein and the equilibria of the substrate A and of the molecule M are reached independently. On the right, the coupling achieves an effective equilibrium constant K_{eff}^A for the substrate A by controlling the intracellular concentration of $[M_{cell}]$ and $[M_{cell}^*]$.

The transporter protein serves to couple the chemical reaction involving M with the movement of substrate A,

$$A_{\text{out}} + M \rightleftharpoons A_{\text{in}} + M^*$$

The effective equilibrium the coupled reaction can achieve is,

$$\frac{[A_{\text{in}}]}{[A_{\text{out}}]} = K_{\text{eq}}^A K_{\text{eq}}^M \frac{[M_{\text{cell}}]}{[M^*_{\text{cell}}]} \tag{12.34}$$

with the effective equilibrium constant,

$$K_{\text{eff}}^A = K_{\text{eq}}^A K_{\text{eq}}^M \frac{[M_{\text{cell}}]}{[M^*_{\text{cell}}]} \gg 1 \tag{12.35}$$

Essentially, the cellular conditions together with the law of mass action provide the free energy utilized to drive the nonequilibrium action of such biomolecular machine with respect to substrate A. This situation is depicted in Figure 12.6 (right).

12.4 ATP as a source of energy

One of the most important examples where coupling to a chemical reaction is used to power a biomolecular machine is the hydrolysis of the adenosine triphosphate (ATP) molecule into adenosine diphosphate (ADP) and inorganic phosphate (Pi),

$$\text{ATP} \rightleftharpoons \text{ADP} + \text{Pi}$$

The equilibrium constant,

$$K_{\text{eq}}^{\text{ATP}} = \frac{[\text{ATP}]}{[\text{ADP}][\text{Pi}]}$$

depends on several factors such as pH and Mg^{2+} concentration, and is equal to 4.8×10^{-6} M^{-1} under physiological conditions. This indicates that the formation of ATP from ADP and Pi is thermodynamically unfavorable. On the basis of the equilibrium constant $K_{\text{eq}}^{\text{ATP}}$, it is often remarked that the chemical bond between the ADP molecule and the inorganic phosphate is "rich" in energy and is a source of the $7.3\,\text{kcal/mol}$ released by the dissociation. However, this argument is somewhat misleading because it pictures the molecule of ATP as some unstable fuel that is irreversibly consumed by ATPase molecular machines. In fact, it is most likely that the chemical bond between ADP and Pi corresponds to some finite stabilization free energy. The free energy from ATP that is harnessed to drive biomolecular machines arises simply from the law of mass action as explained above.

While other chemical reactions are used to drive biological processes, for example, tubulin polymerization relies on the hydrolysis of guanosine triphosphate (GTP) [Wang and Nogales (2005)] and DNA/RNA polymerases use all four bases (ATP, GTP, TTP, and CTP) [Abbondanzieri *et al.* (2005)], the majority of molecular machines in the cell are powered by ATP hydrolysis. For this reason, it is often stated that ATP is the most commonly used "energy currency" of cells for all organisms. Processive motor proteins, such as kinesin, dynein, and myosin, convert the energy from the ATP hydrolysis into mechanical work and motion along microtubules and actin filaments, playing a crucial role in cellular organization [Burgess *et al.* (2003); Kolomeisky and Fisher (2007)] As an example, kinesin is a processive motor that makes a step of 83 Å along microtubules for each ATP molecule hydrolyzed [Vale and Milligan (2000)]. The majority of ATP, about 45% for humans, is hydrolyzed to drive the action of the sodium–potassium pump, which transports 3 Na^+ toward the extracellular side and 2 K^+ toward the intracellular side for each ATP molecule. The pump is part of a large family called P-type ATPase, named upon their ability to hydrolyze ATP and catalyze autophosphorylation of a key conserved aspartate residue within the pump [Palmgren and Nissen (2011)]. Molecular machines that exploit ATP hydrolysis to perform useful work are thermodynamically reversible. In fact, the same principles that are depicted in Figure 12.6 can be exploited to make ATP. For example, artificially steep transmembrane ion gradients make the sodium–potassium run backward to synthesize ATP from ADP and Pi [Garrahan and Glynn (1966); Lew *et al.* (1970)]. This is the mechanism used by ion-translocating rotary F-synthases to drive ATP synthesis from the transmembrane protons gradient [Noji *et al.* (1997); Watanabe *et al.* (2013)]. To avoid all the confusion caused by their names, these proteins can either serve as ATPases or as ATP synthases because the mechanism is reversible.

12.5   Foundational elements of biomolecular models

Membrane transporters, ion channels, biomolecular machines, and motors represent a fertile ground for multiscale computational modeling. Models can help provide a framework to rationally interpret available experiments and formulate the next round of inquiries. It is impossible to lay out an exhaustive review of this rapidly evolving field. Rather, we will end by drawing attention to a few notable examples. Oster and co-workers have presented a very interesting mesoscopic model to illuminate how the stages in ATP synthesis are related to the structural states of F_1F_0 synthases [Xing *et al.* (2005)]. Rudy and co-workers introduced an ambitious multiscale model to simulate the voltage gating of a cardiac K^+ channel, allowing the interpretation of clinical phenotypes [Silva *et al.* (2009)]. Craig and Linke developed a stochastic mechanochemical Brownian dynamics model able to recapitulate myosin V motion with quantitative accuracy [Craig and Linke (2009)]. It shall not come as a surprise that these models rely on many of the fundamental conceptual elements introduced in this book. In fact, most biomolecular models are constructed from the same concepts, which are organized in different ways to reflect the issue of interest for a particular biomolecular system. While the basic foundational "building blocks" are familiar, the design of biomolecular models remain essentially limitless, as the ever-expanding field of biology is full of unknowns and surprises. It is my sincere hope that this book will serve to provide a clear and concise overview of the most important concepts used in biomolecular models and encourage further work in this growing field.

Bibliography

Abbondanzieri, E. A., Greenleaf, W. J., Shaevitz, J. W., Landick, R., and Block, S. M. (2005). Direct observation of base-pair stepping by RNA polymerase, *Nature* **438**, 7067, pp. 460–465.

Alder, B. and Wainwright, T. (1959). Studies in molecular dynamics. 1. General method, *J. Chem. Phys.* **31**, 2, pp. 459–466, doi: 10.1063/1.1730376.

Baker, N. A., Sept, D., Joseph, S., Holst, M. J., and McCammon, J. A. (2001). Electrostatics of nanosystems: Application to microtubules and the ribosome, *Proc. Natl. Acad. Sci. U.S.A.* **98**, 18, pp. 10037–10041.

Berendsen, H., Postma, J., van Gunsteren, W., and Hermans, J. (1981). Interaction models for water in relation to proteins hydration, in B. Pullman (ed.), *Intermolecular Forces* (Reidel, Dordrecht), pp. 331–342.

Born, M. (1920). Volumen und hydratationswarme der ionen, *Z. Phys.* **1**, pp. 45–48.

Bowman, G. R., Pande, V. S., and Noe, F. (2014). An introduction to Markov State Models and their application to long timescale molecular simulations, *Adv. Exp. Med. Biol.* **797**.

Brooks, B. R., Brooks, C. L., III, Mackerell, A. D., Jr., Nilsson, L., Petrella, R. J., Roux, B., Won, Y., Archontis, G., Bartels, C., Boresch, S., Caflisch, A., Caves, L., Cui, Q., Dinner, A. R., Feig, M., Fischer, S., Gao, J., Hodoscek, M., Im, W., Kuczera, K., Lazaridis, T., Ma, J., Ovchinnikov, V., Paci, E., Pastor, R. W., Post, C. B., Pu, J. Z., Schaefer, M., Tidor, B., Venable, R. M., Woodcock, H. L., Wu, X., Yang, W., York, D. M., and Karplus, M. (2009). Charmm: The biomolecular simulation program, *J. Comp. Chem.* **30**, 10, Sp. Iss. SI, pp. 1545–1614, doi: 10.1002/jcc.21287.

Brunger, A., III, C. L. B., and Karplus, M. (1984). Stochastic boundary conditions for molecular dynamics simulations of ST2 water, *Chem. Phys. Letters* **105**, pp. 495–500.

Burgess, S. A., Walker, M. L., Sakakibara, H., Knight, P. J., and Oiwa, K. (2003). Dynein structure and power stroke, *Nature* **421**, 6924, pp. 715–718.

Cardenas, A., Coalson, R., and Kurnikova, M. (2000). Three-dimensional Poisson-Nernst-Planck theory studies: influence of membrane electrostatics on gramicidin A channel conductance. *Biophys. J.* **79**, pp. 80–93.

Chandler, D. (1978). Statistical mechanics of isomerization dynamics in liquids and the transition state approximation, *J. Chem. Phys.* **68**, pp. 2959–2970.

Chandler, D. and Wolynes, P. (1981). Exploiting the isomorphism between quantum theory and classical statistical mechanics of polyatomic fluids, *J. Chem. Phys.* **74**, pp. 4078–4095.

Chandrasekar, S. (1943). Stochastic problem in physics and astronomy, *Rev. Mod. Phys.* **15**, pp. 1–89.

Cornell, W., Cieplak, P., Bayly, C., Gould, I., Jr., K. M., Ferguson, D., Spellmeyer, D., Fox, T., Caldwell, J., and Kollman, P. (1995). A second generation force field for the simulation of proteins and nucleic acids, *J. Am. Chem. Soc.* **117**, pp. 5179–5197.

Craig, E. M. and Linke, H. (2009). Mechanochemical model for myosin V, *Proc. Natl. Acad. Sci. U.S.A.* **106**, 43, pp. 18261–18266.

Davis, M., Madura, J., Luty, B., and McCammon, J. (1991). Electrostatic and diffusion of molecules in solution: Simultations with the University of Houston Brownian Dynamics program, *Comp. Phys. Comm.* **62**, pp. 187–197.

Debye, P. and Hückel, E. (1923). Zur Theorie der Elektrolyte. II. Das Grenzgesetz für die elktrische Leitfähigkeit, *Phys. Z.* **24**, pp. 305–325.

Deng, Y. Q. and Roux, B. (2008). Computation of binding free energy with molecular dynamics and grand canonical monte carlo simulations, *J. Chem. Phys.* **128**, p. 115103.

Deng, Y. Q. and Roux, B. (2009). Computations of standard binding free energies with molecular dynamics simulations, *J. Phys. Chem. B* **113**, pp. 2234–2246.

Dirac, P. A. M. (1929). Quantum mechanics of many-electron systems, *Proc. R. Soc. Lond. A* **123**, pp. 714–733.

Eastman, P., Friedrichs, M. S., Chodera, J. D., Radmer, R. J., Bruns, C. M., Ku, J. P., Beauchamp, K. A., Lane, T. J., Wang, L.-P., Shukla, D., Tye, T., Houston, M., Stich, T., Klein, C., Shirts, M. R., and Pande, V. S. (2013). OpenMM 4: A reusable, extensible, hardware independent library for high performance molecular simulation, *J. Chem. Theor. Comp.* **9**, 1, pp. 461–469, doi: 10.1021/ct300857j.

Ermak, D. (1975). A computer simulation of charged particles in solution. I. Technique and equilibrium properties, *J. Chem. Phys.* **62**, pp. 4162–4196.

Feng, L., Campbell, E. B., and MacKinnon, R. (2012). Molecular mechanism of proton transport in CLC Cl-/H+ exchange transporters, *Proc. Natl. Acad. Sci. U.S.A.* **109**, 29, pp. 11699–11704.

Forrest, L. R., Kramer, R., and Ziegler, C. (2011). The structural basis of secondary active transport mechanisms, *Biochim. Biophys. Acta* **1807**, 2, pp. 167–188.

Fowler, R. and Guggenheim, E. (1939). *Statistical Thermodynamics* (Cambridge University Press).

Frisch, M. J., Trucks, G. W., Schlegel, H. B., Scuseria, G. E., Robb, M. A., Cheeseman, J. R., Scalmani, G., Barone, V., Petersson, G. A., Nakatsuji, H., Li, X., Caricato, M., Marenich, A. V., Bloino, J., Janesko, B. G., Gomperts, R., Mennucci, B., Hratchian, H. P., Ortiz, J. V., Izmaylov, A. F., Sonnenberg, J. L., Williams-Young, D., Ding, F., Lipparini, F., Egidi, F., Goings, J., Peng, B., Petrone, A., Henderson, T., Ranasinghe, D., Zakrzewski, V. G., Gao, J., Rega, N., Zheng, G., Liang, W., Hada, M., Ehara, M., Toyota, K., Fukuda, R., Hasegawa, J., Ishida, M., Nakajima, T., Honda, Y., Kitao, O., Nakai, H., Vreven, T., Throssell, K., Montgomery, J. A., Jr., Peralta, J. E., Ogliaro, F., Bearpark, M. J., Heyd, J. J., Brothers, E. N., Kudin, K. N., Staroverov, V. N., Keith, T. A., Kobayashi, R., Normand, J., Raghavachari, K., Rendell, A. P., Burant, J. C., Iyengar, S. S., Tomasi, J., Cossi, M., Millam, J. M., Klene, M., Adamo, C., Cammi, R., Ochterski, J. W., Martin, R. L., Morokuma, K., Farkas, O., Foresman, J. B., and Fox, D. J. (2016). Gaussian 16 revision c.01, Gaussian Inc. Wallingford CT.

Galochkina, T., Ng Fuk Chong, M., Challali, L., Abbar, S., and Etchebest, C. (2019). New insights into GluT1 mechanics during glucose transfer, *Sci Rep* **9**, 1, p. 998.

Garrahan, P. J. and Glynn, I. M. (1966). Driving the sodium pump backwards to form adenosine triphosphate, *Nature* **211**, 5056, pp. 1414–1415.

Gillespie, D. (1976). General method for numerically simulating stochastic time evolution of coupled chemical-reactions, *J. Comp. Phys.* **22**, 4, pp. 403–434.

Glasstone, S., Laidler, K. J., and Eyring, H. (1941). *Theory of Rate Processes* (McGraw-Hill, New York).

Golden, K., Goldstein, S., and Lebowitz, J. L. (1985). Classical transport in modulated structures, *Phys. Rev. Letters* **55**, pp. 2629–2632.

Gotz, A. W., Williamson, M. J., Xu, D., Poole, D., Le Grand, S., and Walker, R. C. (2012). Routine microsecond molecular dynamics simulations with AMBER on GPUs. 1. Generalized Born, *J Chem Theory Comput* **8**, 5, pp. 1542–1555.

Green, M. (1952). Markoff random processes and the statistical mechanics of time-dependent phenomena, *J. Chem. Phys.* **20**, 8, pp. 1281–1295, doi: 10.1063/1.1700722.

Green, M. (1954). Markoff random processes and the statistical mechanics of time-dependent phenomena. 2. Irreversible processes in fluids, *J. Chem. Phys.* **22**, 3, pp. 398–413, doi:10.1063/1.1740082.

Grosman, C., Zhou, M., and Auerbach, A. (2000). Mapping the conformational wave of acetylcholine receptor channel gating, *Nature* **403**, pp. 773–776.

Grote, R. F. and Hynes, J. T. (1980). The stable states picture of chemical reactions. II. Rate constants for condensed and gas phase reaction models, *J. Chem. Phys.* **73**, pp. 2715–2732.

Hess, B., Kutzner, C., van der Spoel, D., and Lindahl, E. (2008). Gromacs 4: Algorithms for highly efficient, load-balanced, and scalable molecular simulation, *J. Chem. Theo. Comp.* **4**, pp. 435–447.

Humphrey, W., Dalke, A., and Schulten, K. (1996). VMD: visual molecular dynamics, *J Mol Graph* **14**, pp. 33–38.

Im, W. and Roux, B. (2002). Ion permeation and selectivity of OmpF Porin: A theoretical study based on molecular dynamics, Brownian dynamics, and continuum electrodiffusion theory. *J. Mol. Biol.* **322**, pp. 851–869.

Im, W., Beglov, D., and Roux, B. (1998). Continuum solvation model: Electrostatic forces from numerical solutions to the Poisson-Bolztmann equation, *Comp. Phys. Comm.* **111**, pp. 59–75.

Jardetzky, O. (1966). Simple allosteric model for membrane pumps, *Nature* **211**, 5052, pp. 969–970.

Jorgensen, W. L., Chandrasekhar, J., Madura, J. D., Impey, R. W., and Klein, M. L. (1983). Comparison of simple potential functions for simulating liquid water, *J. Chem. Phys.* **79**, pp. 926–935.

Jorgensen, W. L., Maxwell, D. S., and Tirado-Rives, J. (1996). Development and testing of the OPLS all-atom force field on conformational energetics and properties of organic liquids, *J. Am. Chem. Soc.* **118**, pp. 11225–11236.

Kirkwood, J. (1935). Statistical mechanics of fluid mixtures, *J. Chem. Phys.* **3**, pp. 300–313.

Klapper, I., Hagstrom, R., Fine, R., Sharp, K., and Honig, B. (1986). Focusing of electric fields in the active site of cu-zn superoxide dismutase: Effects of ionic strength and amino-acid modification, *Proteins* **1**, p. 47.

Kollman, P. A. (1993). Free energy calculations: Applications to chemical and biochemical phenomena, *Chem. Rev.* **93**, pp. 2395–2417.

Kolomeisky, A. B. and Fisher, M. E. (2007). Molecular motors: A theorist's perspective, *Ann. Rev. Phys. Chem.* **58**, pp. 675–695.

Kramers, H. A. (1940). Brownian motion in a field of force and the diffusion model of chemical reactions, *Physica* **7**, pp. 284–304.

Kubo, R. (1966). The fluctuation-dissipation theorem, *Rev. Mod. Phys.* **29**, pp. 255–284.

Kubo, R. (1957). Statistical-mechanical theory of irreversible processes. 1. General theory and simple applications to magnetic and conduction problems, *J. Phys. Soci. Japan* **12**, 6, pp. 570–586, doi:10.1143/JPSJ.12.570.

Lee, B. and Richards, F. M. (1971). The interpretation of protein structures: Estimation of static accessibility, *J. Mol. Biol.* **55**, 3, pp. 379–400.

Lew, V. L., Glynn, I. M., and Ellory, J. C. (1970). Net synthesis of ATP by reversal of the sodium pump, *Nature* **225**, 5235, pp. 865–866.

Lewis, P. A. W., Goodman, A. S., and Miller, J. M. (1969). A pseudo-random number generator for the System/360, *IBM* **8**, 5052, pp. 136–146.

Lifson, S. and Jackson, J. L. (1962). On the self-diffusion of ions in a polyelectrolyte solution, *J. Phys. Chem.* **36**, pp. 2410–2414.

Läuger, P. (1973). Ion transport through pores: A rate theory analysis, *Biochim. Biophys. Acta* **311**, pp. 423–441.

MacKerell, A. J., Bashford, D., Bellot, M., Dunbrack, R., Evanseck, J., Field, M., Fischer, S., Gao, J., Guo, H., S. Ha, D. J.-M., Kuchnir, L., Kuczera, K., Lau, F., Mattos, C., Michnick, S., Ngo, T., Nguyen, D., Prodhom, B., Reiher III, W., Roux, B., Schlenkrich, M., Smith, J., Stote, R., Straub, J.,

Watanabe, M., Wiorkiewicz-Kuczera, J., and Karplus, M. (1998). All-atom empirical potential for molecular modeling and dynamics studies of proteins, *J. Phys. Chem. B* **102**, pp. 3586–3616.

Massova, I. and Kollman, P. A. (2000). Combined molecular mechanical and continuum solvent approach (MM-PBSA/GBSA) to predict ligand binding, *Perspec. Drug Discov.* **18**, pp. 113–135.

McCammon, J. A. and Straatsma, T. P. (1992). Alchemical free energy simulation, *Ann. Rev. Phys. Chem.* **43**, p. 407.

McCammon, J. A., Gelin, B. R., and Karplus, M. (1977). Dynamics of folded proteins, *Nature* **267**, pp. 585–590.

Merzbacher, E. (1998). *Quantum Mechanics, 3rd Ed.* (John Wiley & Sons, Inc., New York, New York).

Metropolis, N., Rosenbluth, A., Rosenbluth, M., Teller, A., and Teller, E. (1953). Equation of state calculations by fast computing machines, *J. Chem. Phys.* **21**, 6, pp. 1087–1092, doi:10.1063/1.1699114.

Mori, H. (1965). Transport, Collective Motion, and Brownian Motion, *Prog. Theor. Phys.* **33**, pp. 423–455.

Neese, F. (2012). The orca program system, *Wiley Interdiscip. Rev.: Comput. Mol. Sci.* **2**, pp. 73–78.

Nina, M., Beglov, D., and Roux, B. (1997). Atomic radii for continuum electrostatics calculations based on molecular dynamics free energy simulations, *J. Phys. Chem. B* **101**, pp. 5239–5248.

Noji, H., Yasuda, R., Yoshida, M., and Kinosita, K. (1997). Direct observation of the rotation of F1-ATPase, *Nature* **386**, 6622, pp. 299–302.

Palmgren, M. G. and Nissen, P. (2011). P-type ATPases, *Annu Rev Biophys* **40**, pp. 243–266.

Phillips, J., Braun, R., Wang, W., Gumbart, J., Tajkhorshid, E., Villa, E., Chipot, C., Skeel, R., Kale, L., and Schulten, K. (2005). Scalable molecular dynamics with NAMD, *J. Comp. Chem.* **26**, pp. 1781–1802.

Rahman, A. (1964). Correlations in motion of atoms in liquid argon, *Phys. Rev.* **136**, pp. A405–A411.

Razavi, A. M., Khelashvili, G., and Weinstein, H. (2017). A Markov state-based quantitative kinetic model of sodium release from the dopamine transporter, *Sci Rep* **7**, p. 40076.

Rice, S. (1944). Mathematical analysis of random noise, *Bell Syst. Tech. J.* **23**, pp. 282–332, doi:10.1002/j.1538-7305.1944.tb00874.x.

Rice, S. (1945). Mathematical analysis of random noise, *Bell Syst. Tech. J.* **24**, 1, pp. 46–156, doi:10.1002/j.1538-7305.1945.tb00453.x.

Roux, B. (1997). The influence of the membrane potential on the free energy of an intrinsic protein, *Biophys. J.* **73**, pp. 2980–2989.

Roux, B. and Simonson, T. (1999). Implicit solvent models, *Biophys. Chem.* **78**, pp. 1–20.

Roux, B., Yu, H., and Karplus, M. (1990). Molecular basis for the Born model of ion solvation, *J. Phys. Chem.* **94**, pp. 4683–4688.

Schmidt, M., Baldridge, K., Boatz, J., Elbert, S., Gordon, M., Jensen, J., Koseki, S., Matsunaga, N., Nguyen, K., Su, S. J., Windus, T., Dupuis, M., and Montgomery, J. (1993). General atomic and molecular electronic structure system (GAMESS), *J. Comp. Chem.* **14**, pp. 1347–1363.

Shao, Y., Gan, Z., Epifanovsky, E., Gilbert, A. T. B., Wormit, M., Kussmann, J., Lange, A. W., Behn, A., Deng, J., Feng, X., Ghosh, D., Goldey, M., Horn, P. R., Jacobson, L. D., Kaliman, I., Khaliullin, R. Z., Kus, T., Landau, A., Liu, J., Proynov, E. I., Rhee, Y. M., Richard, R. M., Rohrdanz, M. A., Steele, R. P., Sundstrom, E. J., Woodcock, H. L., III, Zimmerman, P. M., Zuev, D., Albrecht, B., Alguire, E., Austin, B., Beran, G. J. O., Bernard, Y. A., Berquist, E., Brandhorst, K., Bravaya, K. B., Brown, S. T., Casanova, D., Chang, C.-M., Chen, Y., Chien, S. H., Closser, K. D., Crittenden, D. L., Diedenhofen, M., DiStasio, R. A., Jr., Do, H., Dutoi, A. D., Edgar, R. G., Fatehi, S., Fusti-Molnar, L., Ghysels, A., Golubeva-Zadorozhnaya, A., Gomes, J., Hanson-Heine, M. W. D., Harbach, P. H. P., Hauser, A. W., Hohenstein, E. G., Holden, Z. C., Jagau, T.-C., Ji, H., Kaduk, B., Khistyaev, K., Kim, J., Kim, J., King, R. A., Klunzinger, P., Kosenkov, D., Kowalczyk, T., Krauter, C. M., Lao, K. U., Laurent, A. D., Lawler, K. V., Levchenko, S. V., Lin, C. Y., Liu, F., Livshits, E., Lochan, R. C., Luenser, A., Manohar, P., Manzer, S. F., Mao, S.-P., Mardirossian, N., Marenich, A. V., Maurer, S. A., Mayhall, N. J., Neuscamman, E., Oana, C. M., Olivares-Amaya, R., O'Neill, D. P., Parkhill, J. A., Perrine, T. M., Peverati, R., Prociuk, A., Rehn, D. R., Rosta, E., Russ, N. J., Sharada, S. M., Sharma, S., Small, D. W., Sodt, A., Stein, T., Stueck, D., Su, Y.-C., Thom, A. J. W., Tsuchimochi, T., Vanovschi, V., Vogt, L., Vydrov, O., Wang, T., Watson, M. A., Wenzel, J., White, A., Williams, C. F., Yang, J., Yeganeh, S., Yost, S. R., You, Z.-Q., Zhang, I. Y., Zhang, X., Zhao, Y., Brooks, B. R., Chan, G. K. L., Chipman, D. M., Cramer, C. J., Goddard, W. A., III, Gordon, M. S., Hehre, W. J., Klamt, A., Schaefer, H. F., III, Schmidt, M. W., Sherrill, C. D., Truhlar, D. G., Warshel, A., Xu, X., Aspuru-Guzik, A., Baer, R., Bell, A. T., Besley, N. A., Chai, J.-D., Dreuw, A., Dunietz, B. D., Furlani, T. R., Gwaltney, S. R., Hsu, C.-P., Jung, Y., Kong, J., Lambrecht, D. S., Liang, W., Ochsenfeld, C., Rassolov, V. A., Slipchenko, L. V., Subotnik, J. E., Van Voorhis, T., Herbert, J. M., Krylov, A. I., Gill, P. M. W., and Head-Gordon, M. (2015). Advances in molecular quantum chemistry contained in the Q-Chem 4 program package, *Molecular Physics* **113**, 2, pp. 184–215, doi: 10.1080/00268976.2014.952696.

Sharp, K., Nicholls, A., Fine, R., and Honig, B. (1991a). Reconciling the magnitude of the microscopic and macroscopic hydrophobic effects, *Science* **252**, pp. 106–109.

Sharp, K., Nicholls, A., Friedman, R., and Honig, B. (1991b). Extracting hydrophobic free energies from experimental data: Relationship to protein folding and theoretical models, *Biochem.* **30**, pp. 9696–9697.

Shaw, D. E., Maragakis, P., Lindorff-Larsen, K., Piana, S., Dror, R. O., Eastwood, M. P., Bank, J. A., Jumper, J. M., Salmon, J. K., Shan, Y., and Wriggers, W. (2010). Atomic-level characterization of the structural dynamics of proteins, *Science* **330**, 6002, pp. 341–346.

Silva, J. R., Pan, H., Wu, D., Nekouzadeh, A., Decker, K. F., Cui, J., Baker, N. A., Sept, D., and Rudy, Y. (2009). A multiscale model linking ion-channel molecular dynamics and electrostatics to the cardiac action potential, *Proc. Natl. Acad. Sci. U.S.A.* **106**, 27, pp. 11102–11106.

Smoluchowski, M. (1916). Drei Vorträge Über Diffusion, Brownsche Molekularbewegung und Koagulation von Kolloidteilchen, *Phys. Z.* **17**, pp. 557–571.

Stillinger, F. (1973). Structure in aqueous solutions of nonpolar solutes from the standpoint of scaled-particle theory, *J. Sol. Chem.* **2**, pp. 141–158.

Stillinger, F. H. and Rahman, A. (1974). Improved simulation of liquid water by molecular dynamics, *J. Chem. Phys.* **60**, pp. 1545–1557.

Tanford, C. (1979). Interfacial free energy and the hydrophobic effect, *Proc. Natl. Acad. Sci. USA* **76**, pp. 4175–4176.

Torrie, G. M. and Valleau, J. P. (1974). Monte Carlo Free Energy Estimates Using Non-Boltzmann Sampling: Application to the Sub-Critical Lennard-Jones Fluid, *Chem. Phys. Lett.* **28**, pp. 578–581.

Tuckerman, M. and Berne, B. (1993). Vibrational-relaxation in simple fluids — Comparison of theory and simulation, *J. Chem. Phys.* **98**, 9, pp. 7301–7318, doi:10.1063/1.464723.

Vale, R. D. and Milligan, R. A. (2000). The way things move: Looking under the hood of molecular motor proteins, *Science* **288**, 5463, pp. 88–95.

Verlet, L. (1967). Computer experiments on classical fluids .I. Thermodynamical properties of Lennard-Jones molecules, *Phys. Rev.* **159**, 1, pp. 98–&, doi: 10.1103/PhysRev.159.98.

Wang, H. W. and Nogales, E. (2005). Nucleotide-dependent bending flexibility of tubulin regulates microtubule assembly, *Nature* **435**, 7044, pp. 911–915.

Warwicker, J. and Watson, H. (1982). Calculation of the electric potential in the active site cleft due to alpha-helix dipoles, *J. Mol. Biol.* **157**, pp. 671–679.

Watanabe, R., Tabata, K. V., Iino, R., Ueno, H., Iwamoto, M., Oiki, S., and Noji, H. (2013). Biased Brownian stepping rotation of FoF1-ATP synthase driven by proton motive force, *Nat. Commun.* **4**, p. 1631.

Xing, J., Liao, J. C., and Oster, G. (2005). Making ATP, *Proc. Natl. Acad. Sci. U.S.A.* **102**, 46, pp. 16539–16546.

Zwanzig, R. W. (1954). High temperature equation of state by a perturbation method, *J. Chem. Phys.* **22**, pp. 1420–1426.

Zwanzig, R. W. (1965). Time-correlation functions and transport coefficients in statistical mechanics, *Ann. Rev. Phys. Chem.* **16**, pp. 67–102.

Zwanzig, R. W. (1988). Diffusion in a rough potential, *Proc. Natl. Acad. Sci. USA* **85**, pp. 2029–2030.

Further reading

The goal of this book is to provide a broad introduction to the key concepts that are used to construct the phenomenological models commonly used to represent the function of large biological macromolecular machines. By choice, the book was not designed for specialists, but for undergraduate and graduate students. For this reason, a great amount of additional material is intentionally left out for the sake of clarity. For readers interested in going further, here is a very succinct list of more advanced textbooks.

Quantum mechanics and *ab initio*

Hehre, W., Radom, L., Schleyer, P. R., and Pople, J. A. (1986). *Ab Initio Molecular Orbital Theory* (John Wiley & Sons, Inc., New York).

Merzbacher, E. (1998). *Quantum Mechanics*, 3rd ed. (John Wiley & Sons, Inc., New York).

Messiah, A. (1976). *Quantum Mechanics* (John Wiley & Sons, New York).

Szabo, A. and Ostlund, N. S. (1982). *Modern Quantum Chemistry: Introduction to Advanced Electronic Structure Theory*, Revised ed. (Dover Publication, Minneola).

Statistical mechanics

Berne, B. J. and Pecora, R. (1976). *Dynamic Light Scattering* (Wiley-Interscience, New York).

Chandler, D. (1987). *Introduction to Modern Statistical Mechanics* (Oxford University Press).

Hill, T. L. (1986). *An Introduction to Statistical Thermodynamics*, 2nd ed. (Dover Publication, Inc., New York).

McQuarrie, D. (1976). *Statistical Mechanics* (Harper and Row, New York).

Risken, H. (1984). *The Fokker-Planck Equation. Methods and Applications* (Springer-Verlag, Berlin).

Zwanzig, R. W. (2001). *Nonequilibrium Statistical Mechanics* (Oxford University Press, New York and Oxford).

Simulation methodologies

Allen, M. and Tildesley, D. (1989). *Computer Simulation of Liquids* (Oxford Science Publications, Clarendon Press, Oxford).

Becker, O. M., MacKerell, A. D., Roux, B., and Watanabe, M. (2001). *Computational Biochemistry and Biophysics* (Marcel Dekker, Inc., New York).

Burkert, U. and Allinger, N. L. (1982). *Molecular Mechanics* (American Chemical Society, Washington).

Chipot, C. and Pohorille, A. (eds.) (2007). *Free Energy Calculations: Theory and Applications in Chemistry and Biology* (Springer-Verlag, Berlin Heidelberg).

Biochemistry and biophysics

Berg, J. M., Tymoczko, J. L., and Stryer, L. (2002). *Biochemistry,* 5th ed. (W. H. Freeman and Co., New York).

Dill, K. and Bromberg, S. (2011). *Molecular Driving Forces: Statistical Thermo Dynamics in Biology, Chemistry, Physics, and Nanoscience,* 2nd ed., ISBN 978-0-8153-4430-8.

Gennis, R. (1989). *Biomembranes: Molecular Structure and Functions* (Springer-Verlag, New York).

Howard, J. (2001). *Mechanics of Motor Proteins and the Cytoskeleton* (Sinauer Associates Inc., Sunderland).

Stryer, L. (1988). *Biochemistry* (W. H. Freeman and Co., New York).

Electrostatics

Jackson, J. D. (1962). *Classical Electrodynamics* (John Wiley & Sons, New York).

Index

CPSIA information can be obtained
at www.ICGtesting.com
Printed in the USA
JSHW041330030921
18407JS00002B/4